R AF

19874

THE REMARKABLE YOUNG MAN

CECIL ROBERTS

THE ~~19874~~ REMARKABLE YOUNG MAN

ARBROATH
PUBLIC
LIBRARY

London
HODDER & STOUGHTON

R ✑ 10. JUN. 1970

FIRST PRINTED 1954

*Made and Printed in Great Britain for Hodder and
Stoughton Limited by The Camelot Press Limited
London and Southampton*

TO

DOROTHY QUICK

CHAPTER I

THE two young men leaned out of the window of their apartment in the Piazza di Spagna. The afternoon sun of a November day still had some warmth in it. At the top of the great flight of marble steps, on a terrace in front of the twin-towered church of Trinità dei Monti, old people and nurses with their charges sat sunning themselves, while the creeping shadow of the tall obelisk crowning the steps marked the vanishing hours.

At the foot of the steps, the noble gift of a French Ambassador, lay the Piazza di Spagna, the busiest centre of Papal Rome. It took the form of two triangles united by a narrow space where the elder Bernini had built a curious fountain. Amid the many fountains whose murmur gave enchantment to the bright noons and moonlit nights of haunted Rome, Bernini's effort had achieved originality; it was in the form of a floating boat, itself flooded by an interior fountain.

On the steps looking down on this elliptical basin, until the hour of noon, gathered a picturesque crowd of Italians; near-naked Roman heroes, dark-eyed Madonnas, Holy Infants, nymphs, fauns, villains, and handsome lads ready to pose as Mercury, Bacchus or Antinous, according to the requirements of Rome's large colony of artists. At noon they vanished and the erstwhile gods of the marble steps consumed their spaghetti prior to the siesta that flung a pall of silence over the Eternal City.

The northern end of the unlevel and unpaved Piazza looked like the encampment of a fair, with innumerable caravans ranged row upon row. But these were not caravans, they were the coaches of the nobility, predominantly

English, now gathered in Rome for the fashionable winter season. By this year, 1820, Europe had recovered from the Napoleonic Wars that had devastated it. The terrible Boney had been locked up on St Helena. Relieved from the nightmare of the bellicose Emperor, Europe resumed its former habits, and the exiled Pope returned to the Papal States from which he had been brutally ravished. So little rancour had the aristocratic Pius VII displayed that almost all the Napoleonic clan, rudely evicted from their thrones and principalities, had gathered in Rome, the recipient of Papal protection. In her palace Madame Mère, the Emperor's dignified old mother, attended by her brother Cardinal Fesch, quietly kept court.

The fashion of the Grand Tour, which throughout the eighteenth century had seen the scions of the English nobility travelling about Italy, accompanied by grooms, valets, and clergymen in the rôle of tutors, had lingered on into the nineteenth century. Byron as Childe Harold had given new glamour to the Continental landscape. Suddenly it became the fashion to winter in Rome. Over the mountain passes, down into the Lombardian plain the English coaches came jolting. They were formidable equipages, their roofs loaded with trunks, their panels blazoned with coats of arms, the grooms in household liveries. Since one coach could not transport the comforts its owner demanded, other vehicles carried the necessary beds, linen, cooking utensils and oddments of furniture. Experience had taught the luxurious itinerant aristocracy that rows of paintings by Raphael, Titian, Giorgione and other masters, salons damask-lined, with vistas of crystal chandeliers in the noble palaces they rented for the season, did not compensate for the simple home comforts so sadly missing. Roman footmen and grooms were ten-a-penny but a French chef picked up *en route* in Paris and added to an English butler minimised the defects of foreign residence. The English milords with untaxed incomes of twenty, thirty and forty thousand pounds a year saw no reason for petty economies. In the burst of prosperity following the Napoleonic Wars they were masters of the world with their good gold sovereigns, their sound landed estates.

The two young Englishmen looking down from their window on the assembled coaches of the British colony in Rome had neither sovereigns nor estates. At that precise moment, after three weeks' residence in Rome, they were worried about their funds. Everything was always a little dearer than they had hoped. One of them, John Keats, warned that the rigours of an English winter threatened his death at the age of twenty-five, had gathered together a few pounds of his shrunken patrimony. The other, Joseph Severn, his senior by a year, had accompanied him in a spirit of selfless devotion with practically no funds, all his hopes being based on the fact that he might succeed in winning the Travel Scholarship of the Royal Academy, whose Gold Medal, awarded to its most promising student, he had gained that spring.

When he had announced his departure for Rome to the Severn family crowding the humble home at Shoreditch, his choleric father, outraged by such a foolhardy proposal, had knocked him down. One of Severn's last memories, as the carriage with his trunk bore him away to the London docks in the chill September dawn, was of his dear mother saying brokenly, "Pray God for your poor father. He doesn't know what he is doing." Young Joseph Severn knew well what he was doing. He was attending one endowed with immortal genius, though only a devoted few recognised this. He had come with his friend to Rome because its glorious sunshine and gentle air might defeat the enemy consuming him. Even if he had hazarded everything in his career, and alienated his father, what did it matter if John Keats was saved?

So here they were, on an afternoon of November 1820, with very few pounds in their pockets, leaning out of the window of a two-roomed apartment at 26 Piazza di Spagna, found for them by kindly Dr Clark, a local English physician. What if they had little money, if a shadow haunted them? They were young, they were in Rome whose intoxicating pageant was spread out before them.

They could not have been better placed. They had one large and one small room on the second floor of a house that stood at the foot of the great marble steps. Two windows looked down on to the Piazza; one window of the narrow lofty room where Keats slept overlooked the steps and had also a view over the Piazza. Out of this window in the russet-orange façade they now leaned. They could see above them, rising to the skyline, the obelisk erected by Pius VII, and the towers of the Church of Trinità dei Monti. One of these towers carried a clock with a six-hour dial, the other a sun-dial. As they looked up at the towers bathed in afternoon sunlight it was four o'clock, the hour of the Corso on the Pincio, that ilex and pine-crowned plateau above the Piazza del Popolo from whose balustraded terrace one saw all Rome in the valley of the Tiber.

"There he is!" cried Severn, and waved his hand to a young man in the Piazza below.

An elegant, youthful figure raised a beaver hat in response to their salutation. A few minutes later there was a knock on the sitting-room door. Severn and Keats left the window to greet their visitor, Lieutenant Elton.

He was a young man of a singularly bright disposition, but unhappily he was haunted by the same threat of consumption. They owed their introduction to Elton to Dr Clark who was also his physician. In bearing and appearance nothing indicated his impaired health. Tall, well-built, his neat head was crowned by black curls that set off the broad brow and the ruddy complexion. Good breeding revealed itself in voice and gesture. The son of a Sussex squire, he had seen service as an Ensign at Waterloo. Then, suddenly, in his twenty-fifth year, at the opening of a promising military career, a weakness of the lungs had caused him to winter in Rome. There was in his manner, in the gaiety with which he enjoyed his life in the fashionable circles of this lively city no suggestion of ill-health. He rode, danced and fluttered a dozen hearts with the roguish sparkle of his eyes. He was dressed to-day, as always, with the greatest elegance. The lavender pantaloons that clung to his slim legs were understrapped to a pair of neat shoes. He wore a powder-blue cutaway coat, with sleeves puffed at the shoulders, snowy frilled shirt and a pale blue waistcoat, shaped to his youthful waist. A cameo pin rested in his cream stock. His tall beaver hat had a rakish curl to its brim.

He had brought to Rome a pair of fine hunters and had soon established himself with the Roman hunt as a spirited rider. A young man of ample fortune, he was much sought after by the English dowagers and mammas with daughters for disposal. Yet with all this he was modest and affable in manner. From their first meeting he had shown himself singularly friendly to these two young men who were neither of his station nor his tastes. Severn immediately responded to this magnetic personality. Keats, more reserved and suspicious of any form of patronage, had been slower to surrender to the young dandy, but within a fortnight Elton had won him over. When Dr Clark had warned Keats against too much exercise amid the exciting scenes of Rome, it was Elton who had suggested that they should make short excursions on horseback. So while Severn pursued his art studies, Elton went riding with Keats. They rode along the banks of the Tiber, from which the massive old Castle of St Angelo raised its bronze angel above the ancient mausoleum of the Emperor Hadrian, or they went out by the Porta del Popolo as far as the Milvio Bridge, where Constantine had defeated Maxentius and thereby established the first era of Christian Rome. In time Elton fell under the spell of his reticent companion whose melancholy added to the strength of an impressive personality.

On horseback their physical disparity was not noticeable. On foot Elton quite dwarfed the diminutive Keats, whose broad-shouldered figure was only an inch over five feet. There was personal beauty in this liveryman's son as well as distinction of mind. His head was crowned by a mass of shining rust-gold hair, his eyes had a singular brilliance when he was animated in speech. Of his poetry, confined to three small books, Elton knew nothing, and had he read them he would scarcely have perceived any merit in them, for his mind was wholly engaged by pretty faces or the lines of a well-bred hunter. He could sing a ballad as well as he could dance a quadrille or hit a bull's eye at five hundred paces. Never once in their talks had Keats embarrassed him with glimpses of an æsthetic world wherein he would have felt lost. The poet was a sound little fellow with no fancy airs, Elton reported later, when someone asked him what John Keats had been like.

The three young men had contracted a pleasant habit. Every afternoon, at the hour of the Grand Concourse, they had gone up the steps and along the terrace by the Villa Medici to the park on the Pincio, where all the fashion of Rome, in carriages and on horseback, foregathered at the hour before sunset.

"Well, are you ready?" asked Elton, stroking the crown of his beaver with a gloved hand.

"You make us look like a pair of shabby crows," said Severn, taking down his hat. He reached for a loose cloak, draping it over the shoulders of Keats, who protested. Then they went down the stairs into the Piazza.

They mounted the marble steps slowly, lingering at the top of each flight to turn and look over Rome in the valley below. Above them the Church of Trinità dei Monti shone in the afternoon sun. Then along the high terrace shady with ilex trees they walked past the twin-towered Villa Medici, with its belvedere, once the property of the great Medici family. It had been acquired by Napoleon and made the new home of the French Academy founded by Louis XIV for young French artists studying in Rome. Galileo had been confined there during his trial before the Inquisition. It had housed Velasquez on his visit to Rome.

"When you win the *Prix de Rome*," said Elton, chaffingly to Severn, "we might buy you a palace like that to live in —it's time we had a British Academy here. I want to show you something," he added, and led them across the road to a pair of massive bronze doors at the entrance. "Do you see this dint?" he asked, passing his hand over it. "When Queen Christina of Sweden abdicated and came to Rome she dined with the Pope at the Castle St Angelo. They fired a cannon in her honour and forgot it was loaded. The ball traversed Rome and made this dint!"

"How warm the door is in the afternoon sun!" said Keats, passing his hand over the metal.

They mounted an incline and presently came to a large open space planted with oleander, ilex, cypress and palm trees. In the centre there was a round open space. On it carriages and equestrians slowly circulated.

It was a beautiful scene. The rosy level light of evening fell on a dark background of majestic pine trees. The slender trunks of these giants were canopied with dense foliage and stood dramatically grouped against a jade-green evening sky. This pine-clad plateau, where now the Roman aristocracy circulated, their open carriages drawn by splendid horses in the charge of liveried grooms, was bounded on the west side by a low marble balustrade. From a precipitous height they beheld the famous panorama of Rome. Immediately below lay the great open space of the Piazza del Popolo and the ancient gateway to the Via Flaminia, known to the Roman legions, the barbarian hordes and successive conquerors marching down from the north upon the Eternal City. In the valley of the Tiber, beyond a maze of towers, domes and belvederes of churches and palaces, were the tortoise-like roof of the ancient Pantheon, the embattled keep of the Castle St Angelo and, more distant, the vast dome of St Peter's. It stood there, gigantic and symbolic with its cross silhouetted against the glowing west, while to its left, black against the horizon, ranged the dense pine woods crowning the long Janiculum Hill.

The three young Englishmen had seen this panorama for almost two weeks, a sight of such majesty as was beyond all words. Turning from it, and joining a small group of spectators, their attention was held by the human pageant. Here before them was paraded the wealth, pride and arrogance of living Rome. The equipages of the princes, dukes and counts of Roman society circulated slowly in the evening sun. The women in their carriages bowed proudly to their friends, formally greeting each other. A number of gallants on horseback attended them. The English aristocracy mingled with the Roman. Missing from this social scene were the great coaches of the Cardinals. They drove to the Porta Pia, where they descended and took a little exercise, attended by their gentlemen and valets. The Church was not wholly absent from the Pincio for a few scarlet-clad monsignors accompanied the great ladies of Rome in their carriages.

The horses were superb, as also their accoutrements of crested harnesses and hammercloths embroidered with coronets. They were attended by grooms in the liveries of famous houses, the Colonna, Borghese, Massimo, Barberini, Caetani, Ludovisi, Ruspoli, Doria, Chigi and Corsini, great palaces and villas that were part of the history and glory of Rome.

Elton, popular in society by reason of his charm and handsome address, and reinforced with an adequate knowledge of Italian, knew many in this glowing concourse of beautiful women and superb horses. His hat was constantly raised as smiling ladies responded to his bows. The three young Englishmen drew many eyes. They were good-looking, two of them arrestingly so, and the gradation of their figures, one commandingly tall, one medium in height, one almost dwarf-like, attracted attention.

"Ah, here's the enemy!" exclaimed Elton as a particularly impressive equipage came into sight. On the box-seat were two resplendent coachmen in green and yellow liveries, with white wigs surmounted by peaked velvet caps. A pair of young footmen in gilt-braided coats and wide cockaded hats sat behind. In the carriage there was an elderly, white-bearded man, dark-featured. A lady sat stiffly beside him, her black bodice offset by two long strings of pearls. The equipage in its lavish ostentation was a little too spectacular even in this vivid scene. The carriage of the Duchess Cesarini-Sforza, an old lady with a mass of white hair mounted on her head *à la Pompadour*, mantilla-clad, seemed demure in comparison, and the equipage of the Princess Jerome Bonaparte, Napoleon's German sister-in-law, who was accompanied by her small son, Prince Jerome, and a nurse carrying the little Princess Mathilde, seemed positively shabby.

The enemy, identified by Elton, was one of the most

remarkable men in Rome. He was Prince Giovanni Torlonia, Duke of Bracciano, famous for his wealth, his entertainments and his horses. These horses, drawn from English stables, won all the prizes in the great Corso race year after year. Obscure in origin, Torlonia by his adroitness had built up a powerful banking business. Banker to Pius VI and Pius VII, he had emerged from the Napoleonic Wars richer than before. Having successively rescued the Vatican from financial disaster in these tempestuous years, he had become the confidant of the Pope, and had been ennobled by him for his services. He ate up the estates of the impoverished Roman aristocracy, adding the titles that went with them to his own. He possessed provinces, churches, palaces, castles, and whole squares and streets. He had married his sons into the great families of Colonna, Chigi and Ruspoli. His first son he made Duke of Marino and gave him a fortune. "But he's a fool and he won't have my business. That'll go to Alessandro—he's clever. If he plays his cards well—he's married a Colonna—he'll make his son Pope." But time cheated Torlonia. His son's beautiful wife went mad and they had no son.

"Why do you call him the enemy?" asked Severn as the banker's carriage went by.

"Oh, if you only knew what a cantankerous old boy he is!" exclaimed Elton. "I went to his bank with a perfectly good draft one day. His minions smelt it all over and then showed it to him. It was post-dated a month, that was all that was wrong with it. I was taken to see him. I explained that the Elton credit was perfectly sound, that I merely wanted my monthly allowance a little in advance. And what do you think the old rascal said? He was sure my father would be indebted to him for not encouraging me to exceed my allowance! And then old Shylock gave himself away completely—said he'd cash it for a ten per cent. discount! Outrageous! But of course I had to do it."

"Were you that pressed?" asked Keats. "That's how bankers get rich."

"Yes. I just had to have it. A charming little friend had seen some earrings in the Via Condotti and it was her birthday in a couple of days," said Elton.

They left the concourse and were about to cross one of the avenues bordered with oleanders when a sudden patter of hooves fell on their ears. Another carriage was going towards the rendezvous on the Pincio. At once they recognised the equipage. It was unmistakable and unique. It drew all eyes, as it was intended to do, by its opulence and by the character of the woman who sat in the shallow yellow carriage attended by her latest *cavaliere servente*, Signor Pacini.

The three young Englishmen had seen her a few days earlier in this same concourse of which she was the most famous spectacle. They were aware also that she had seen them and had taken no trouble to disguise her interest. The Princess Pauline Borghese, Napoleon's notorious sister, at the age of thirty-seven had not lost her vivid interest in any good-looking young man. And here were three young men, obviously English, of whom one, divinely tall, was exceedingly handsome even in comparison with his good-looking friends. The third was too short for her taste. She required of any man that his legs should be long.

The Princess's carriage was emblazoned with the coats of arms of a royal house of France and a noble house of Rome. The eagle of Napoleon and the eagle of the Borghese were surmounted by the imperial N. The shallow vehicle drawn by six paired horses had two postillions astride, clad in scarlet and gold liveries, a large monogram embroidered in gold on their sleeves.

B

Their short cutaway jackets set off their slim waists and tight kid breeches. They were olive-skinned Italians in the first pride of their youth. Behind the resplendent carriage, erect and impassive, two negro pages in crimson jackets gave a bizarre note to the equipage, emphasised by a touch of eccentricity. Their crisp, woolly curls were pomaded with white powder, like a pastrycook's confection, in startling contrast with their smooth black faces.

In the carriage the Princess sat enthroned, arrogance merging with allure. She was still a beautiful woman with a petite figure. It was a figure familiar to the whole world, for who had not seen Canova's masterpiece, *Victorious Venus in Repose*, the voluptuous statue of a woman naked from the thighs up? Her outraged husband, Prince Camillo Borghese, had for a time locked it away in a gallery of the vast Palazzo Borghese where, on her marriage, she had made her home. A Venus indeed, but never at any time in repose, commented Rome. Indifferent to her successive amours, Prince Camillo had finally fled to the refuge of an *amie* from the tantrums, extravagances and indiscretions of a nymphomaniac. He was now living with the Duchess della Rovere in a Florentine palace. Aggrieved that he should find happiness in another woman's arms, the Princess besought the Papal powers to enforce her husband's return.

The young men who now saw her carriage advancing towards them knew something if not all of her turbulent story. They had seen the famous statue, exhibited for a small tip by a butler in the great Borghese palace. Keats had been more disgusted than shocked by it. "Beautiful bad taste," he commented, but Severn admitted to being overwhelmed by the sheer genius of Canova's technique. Elton whole-heartedly surrendered to the undisguised lasciviousness of the work. "What a woman! What breasts, torso, neck!" he exclaimed.

The carriage companion of the Princess Pauline Borghese was Rome's newest sensation. She had found him, her twentieth or thirtieth lover, for his place in the hierarchy was beyond exact numerical determination, one evening at the opera. The composition of a young maestro had been enthusiastically received. The Princess had not listened to the music, for she had chatted in her box throughout the performance with Prince Rospigliosi and Count Rasponi, young gallants with classical heads that somehow failed to evoke any degree of passion in her. Then before the curtain, bowing to the applauding audience, came the young, dark and handsome young composer. At a glance her interest was evoked. Ten minutes later he was presented to her.

He was a Sicilian, Signor Giovanni Pacini. That had been the name of the young doctor of a former famous affair six years ago when the Austrians had sought to send her as a prisoner to Austria. They arrested her, enraged by the undeniable fact that on the Isle of Elba she had aided her brother's escape and financed it with the gift of her diamond necklace, thus supporting his last desperate venture in the Hundred Days. She thereupon staged an illness and produced with the young doctor's aid a list of symptoms that overwhelmed the greybeard Austrian physician sent to report on the possibility of moving her. Successful in this ruse, she moved later of her own accord to Bagni di Lucca, taking with her the handsome young Dr Pacini. That affair had run for some months, until, bored, she dismissed him. How strange that this latest recruit should carry the name Pacini! She drove away with him that evening from the theatre. He became as much an object of her household as the giant negro footman who carried her, wrapped in a white towel, from her bath to the couch where she had a pedicure while her admirers sat around.

Rome, seeing Pacini playing the piano at her soirées and attending her in her carriage, was not scandalised; it was amused. For how could a society, probably the most corrupt in Europe, at once impecunious, arrogant, effete and immoral, show itself censorious to this audacious cocotte who had married into the great house of Borghese? The glamorous Napoleonic tradition still lingered, though its founder languished in St Helena. Here in Rome almost every great lady exhibited her *cavaliere servente* while a complaisant husband played truant with his mistress. Behind the great names, behind the impressive façades of the palaces that housed them, lay spiritual and material bankruptcy. While footmen in their shabby liveries escorted the guests through corridors of dim salons decorated with rare tapestries, statuary and the masterpieces of Raphael, Tintoretto, Bellini and Correggio, vast mausoleums of decayed splendour, their proud owners gossiped, gamed and fornicated. At any moment it seemed as if these ancient palaces, housing families that claimed descent from the senators of imperial Rome, might collapse in a cloud of dust and scandal.

In such a society the notorious adventures of the beautiful Princess Borghese were yet another diversion. The story of her affairs titillated a world that made no distinction between fame and notoriety. From the poverty of a Marseilles back street where the Corsican exiles had been driven to accept public assistance, Pauline had risen resplendently with the Napoleonic star. Exquisite in figure, with a flawless Greek profile, an oval face, the bust and shoulders of a goddess, and a mass of dark curls above a pair of eyes that made every man she looked upon her slave, she had the soul of a courtesan and the temperament of a *gamine*. She had also to her credit, beyond any degree possessed by the rest of her family, a selfless devotion to her brother. When in the hour of final ruin at

Waterloo the Allies captured his carriage, they found in a secret tray a collar of priceless diamonds, her contribution to his last desperate gamble. She had gone to him at Elba after the Empress deserted him and now, while he sat brooding in St Helena, she intrigued for his release and pleaded with the obdurate British Foreign Secretary to be allowed to share his exile. In the heart of a strumpet burned a flame of devotion to her beloved brother. For the others, Louis, Lucien, Jerome, all here under the wing of Madame Mère, and Joseph in America, she had little but contempt.

Princess Pauline had noticed the three young Englishmen the previous day. The tallest of them, an elegant figure, who had looked upon her with undisguised admiration, evoked her interest for a dual reason. He was not only an attractive young man; he bore a singular resemblance to another whose attachment to her had ended in deep tragedy. Incapable though she was of any depth of feeling in regard to her past lovers, young Jules Canonville had not wholly faded from her memory. He was perhaps the handsomest and most passionate of all her conquests, a rising young colonel of thirty, attached to Berthier's staff. She had first seen him in Paris, which soon rang with the news of her latest liaison. The young colonel, dazzled, threw all discretion to the winds, oblivious that Napoleon, enraged by his sister's escapades, was watching her with a censorious eye.

The Emperor had given her a magnificent sable-lined pelisse, a present from Czar Alexander after their momentous meeting at Tilsit in 1807. His anger knew no bounds when one day at a review he beheld it on the dashing figure of young Canonville. Within twenty-four hours he was despatched from France on a hazardous mission. But distance only increased young Canonville's devotion, while the intransigent Pauline played Andromache to her gallant Hector. His passionate letters fed her vanity, and without considering that she was endangering his career she read them aloud to the court of admirers who flocked to her palace in Paris. Then at Borodino, in the bloody battle where thirty-two thousand young Frenchmen uselessly sacrificed their lives to gain the shell of Moscow, the gallant Jules lay in a welter of the dead. A comrade, finding the body and removing his papers, came upon a bloodstained portrait of the Princess Pauline. It was compromising. "I alone saw it and destroyed it," reported the friend to the Princess.

Poor Jules, so gallant in the field and in the boudoir! She thought of him now as she saw this young man who had evoked his memory. Perhaps it was past happiness as much as present interest that caused her to throw him a coquettish glance, inclining her head in an almost imperceptible bow. It was not in vain. Before the carriage had passed the young man had swept off his hat.

"I'll be damned—did you see that?" cried Elton jubilantly to his companions. "She raked me fore and aft!"

Severn was too surprised to make immediate comment, but before any words had come from his lips they were arrested by the expression on Keats's face. He had turned white and was trembling with a look of mingled anguish and horror. Then to his friends' astonishment, they saw tears welling in his eyes.

"My dear fellow—what is it, what upsets you so? Not her, surely? I'm——" began Elton, solicitously. The sentence went unfinished.

"We will not speak of it—please, I beg you!" cried Keats, chokingly. "Let us go!"

He turned and abruptly went off, leaving his companions to follow. Elton bewildered and distressed, looked at Severn. "Have I done anything to hurt him? Surely it wasn't our little flirtation? It couldn't be that?" he asked.

"It's something difficult to explain. Look, he mustn't walk at that pace!" cried Severn in agitation. In silence they hurried after the vanishing figure.

II

That evening in their rooms on the Piazza di Spagna they were very quiet. Neither of the two young men made any reference to the incident on the Pincio. Happily, something diverted their thoughts. A piano had been delivered to the little apartment. It was an extravagance that cost seven scudi a month. The idea had arisen one day when Severn talked of the Royal Academy School in London where he had studied under the splenetic Fuseli. His teacher had known the great Haydn and had painted his portrait when the composer had made a triumphant visit to London. Keats had expressed his love of Haydn's music. Severn, anxious to do anything that would divert his friend from brooding over his condition, had suggested hiring a piano. Their kindly doctor had at once abetted the suggestion, and now here was the piano, with a liberal supply of music from Dr Clark's wife, including some of Haydn's symphonies.

Severn, an indifferent pianist, began to play. The pleasure on Keats's face as he raced with many false notes through Haydn's score gave him much delight. Keats's fit of brooding was dispelled. The incident on the Pincio lay heavy on Severn's mind. He knew well what had provoked the outburst there.

Later, looking back on that evening, Severn recalled it as one of the happiest of their time in Rome. A shadow had been over them through all those weeks since their departure from London in the *Maria Crowther*, a clumsy schooner of only a hundred and thirty tons. Fate had seemed against them from the beginning. Aware of the sentence of death upon him since that hour when he had examined by candle-light the bedsheet on which he had coughed blood, before retiring, Keats had embarked in a mood of resignation to his fate. The journey had been dreadful. For ten days they were thrown about the Channel in a tempest. Five passengers were crammed in a dark smelly cabin. Ill-fate had designed that one of their companions, a young and pretty woman, was in the last stages of consumption and, like Keats, she had been ordered to winter in Italy as the only chance of survival. The ship encountered fearful storms in the Bay of Biscay until calm came as they lay off Cape St Vincent. After four weeks they sailed into the Bay of Naples, but their pleasure in its famed beauty was dashed by the news that owing to the fact that typhus had been reported from London they would be kept in quarantine for ten days. Storms, bad food and cramped quarters had worn them out, and now they had to stew on what seemed like the threshold of paradise, with its vivid blue sky, sparkling water and the glowing curve of the bay with villa-crowned hills under the bright October sun. Before their quarantine had ended, the scene had been overclouded and Naples was blotted out in a deluge of rain.

They went ashore at last on the first day of November in a damp fog that shrouded the harbour. The young woman with them was visibly dying and the anxious brother who had come to greet her wondered if she would survive the landing. Severn, descending to the cabin to collect his friend, was horrified to discover him coughing violently, his coat stained with the blood of a new hæmorrhage. Somehow he controlled his fainting senses and managed the journey through the evil-smelling streets to their lodging at the Hôtel d'Inghilterra.

It was a Naples still in the throes of a revolution. King Ferdinand had gone back on his promise of a constitution. The next day he fled. The kingdom was threatened with another foreign occupation. The degradation of the Neapolitans was beyond belief. It added to their depression.

Something more than physical sickness lay upon Keats. He was tormented by frustrated love. For more than a year the misery and ecstasy of his passion for Fanny Brawne had fevered his mind. Moods of intense jealousy goaded him to the bitterest recrimination of a young woman whose natural gaiety of spirit appeared to him as faithless levity. Conscious that he could never marry the girl he loved so passionately, he had agitated himself, even while being devotedly nursed in the Brawne household, by imaginary evidence of Fanny's flightiness. A letter from her, delayed by a servant for two days, was construed as a conspiracy against him. For Fanny to be happy in the presence of others was torture. That she could enjoy life seemed to him a proof that she lacked any depth of feeling towards him. They had difficult scenes, remonstrances and accusations. Consumed with passion, to have met her had been a misfortune; to love her, without any hope of consummation of his passion, seemed a perverse trick of Fate.

It was the burden of this fate upon his sick soul that had caused the outburst on the Pincio. The gaiety of young Elton, evoked by that worthless woman, had been unbearable. In that arch glance Keats had seen his own coquettish Fanny now for ever beyond sight and touch. He had hurried away, terrified that the eyes of his companions might plumb his misery.

In Naples there had been moments of happiness. The fresh scene, the beauty of the Italian day had quietened his spirit temporarily. A kindly letter had awaited him from Percy Bysshe Shelley in Pisa. It was an invitation to visit him. This was the second generous gesture of a man Keats hardly knew, a poet like himself, notorious for having been sent down from Oxford for avowed atheism, the husband of a wife he had discarded for the unsavoury Godwin's daughter, a husband denounced in the public courts for callous conduct that had driven a wretched girl-wife to suicide. The world heard Shelley's name with horror. Keats had known nothing but kindness and generosity from him.

For a time the only expression of Keats's misery had been made in letters to his friend Brown, whose house he had once shared in those terrible days after he had nursed his young brother Tom on his deathbed. He had written to Brown during those first days in Naples, before they set off in a hired carriage for Rome: "I am well enough this morning to write you a short calm letter, if that can be called one in which I am afraid to speak of what I would fainest dwell upon . . . perhaps it may relieve the load of wretchedness which presses upon me. The persuasion that I will see her no more will kill me."

It truly was killing him, as Severn saw too plainly. In his devotion to Keats, at the prompting of a devoted circle believing intensely in the genius of the poet, he had undertaken to bring him to Italy though jeopardising his own career. His first success, the winning of the Royal Academy's Gold Medal, had created enemies. It was borne upon him that the Council might hesitate to award him the three-year travelling scholarship, however much he merited it; a student who had gone abroad was either independent or presumptuous in thinking that the prize would be his. But these considerations had been waived by him in the face of Keats's necessity.

Now, here in Rome, despite Keats's solicitous regard for his career, it required much resolution to set time apart for work on his Academy canvas. He was companion-housekeeper and nurse. He had to do the shopping, struggling with a strange language, make beds, clean the apartment and prepare such meals as they had not ordered in. The bought meals were of such a wretched nature that finally they drove Keats to revolt. One evening, in the presence of the boy who had carried in their dinner from a nearby *trattoria*, he went to the window and threw it out on to the steps in protest against its miserable quality. His violent gesture provided a dozen Roman cats with a feast. But it was effective and resulted in a better meal appearing after a short interval.

They had only one fireplace, in the little bedroom occupied by Keats. The November evenings were chilly immediately following sundown. Severn, often provoked to a display of temper, struggled to light the fire. The pine wood was slow to start burning, but once kindled it was consumed with alarming speed, for wood was costly and strained their tight budget. Even more trying was the unveiled hostility of their landlady, Signora Angeletti. She suspected the condition of one of them, though Severn made desperate efforts to keep her in ignorance. Unhappily the entrance to their rooms was through an outer room in which she lived. No one came or went, no errand was performed except under her mean, dark eyes. Twice she endeavoured to discover from Dr Clark the true nature of the *giovane Inglese's* sickness. He pacified her fears, assuring her that it was not a case of fever. The young man was extremely delicate and must rest.

There had now grown up between the two friends an intense devotion. Keats's sturdy and introspective nature was quite different from that of the volatile, enthusiastic Severn's. There was in the artist a natural gaiety that shone in his delicate features and expressive eyes. He felt himself on the threshold of life and success. The intoxication of the Roman scene, the sunlit days, the glowing life of the streets, the treasures of the galleries seemed like a transition to Paradise after that overcrowded little house in a mean court in Shoreditch. The Severns were a devoted family, but they lived under the dominance of a choleric father. Later Severn had taken refuge with a married sister, while pursuing his Academy studies.

Rome would have been an absolute Paradise except for the fact that the mental and physical suffering of one he loved was ever before his eyes. There were occasions, however, when the Keats who had charmed his Hampstead friends, the young man with the spirit of genius shining through the translucent flesh, was glimpsed again in a sudden ecstasy over a phrase of a book or the fall of light on the Spanish Steps in the golden glow of evening. He loved the dark dramatic beauty of the Roman pine woods, the lore of temple or obelisk, the voices of many fountains, more vocal in the night when the moon turned them to silver.

Between them now there were no secrets. There had been a memorable evening in Naples, while a pitiless rain drummed on the pavement, when in the confines of their room Keats, driven to intolerable despair, had bared his soul. The whole tragedy of frustrated love consuming him suddenly became vocal. It was a passion that would destroy him, he confessed. It had already robbed him of the desire to live. In vain Severn had tried to console him. Never again after that scene had Keats made further reference to his despair, but the outburst on the Pincio that had so amazed Elton had presented no enigma to Severn. Twice letters had come from Fanny Brawne to Keats. Other letters had been eagerly opened; hers had gone unopened into a drawer. It was as if they were incendiary and would consume him. Severn made no comment. He observed in sorrow.

CHAPTER II

I

IN the days following the advent of the piano, beautiful sunny days, Keats was in a less despondent mood. Severn began to feel that perhaps they were fighting a chimera, something that would vanish in this bright scene. Elton rode out daily with Keats while Severn went off to study in the Vatican Galleries, making good progress with his Royal Academy picture. He bore a letter from its famous president, Sir Thomas Lawrence, to the great Canova, the dominant figure of artistic Rome with his international reputation and his standing with the Vatican. An old man now, near the close of his life, loaded with honours, the Marquis Canova had travelled a long way since, a stonemason's small son, he had modelled a lion in butter that brought him to the attention of a kindly Venetian patrician. He was now building his own Pantheon up in Possagno, the little village in the foothills of the Friulian Alps whence he had come. Here in Rome, off the Corso, he occupied a famous studio where workmen roughed out the statues commissioned by kings and statesmen for the royal palaces and galleries of Europe.

There was a vogue for classical sculpture, following the fashion created by young English milords making the Grand Tour. In the past hundred years many ancient sites throughout Italy had been feverishly excavated. The classical statuary recovered from Pompeii, Herculaneum and Tivoli, and from the sites of ancient villas, did not suffice to supply all the great houses of England to which galleries and museums had been added and whose grounds were laid out with terraces and alcoves adorned with Greek and Roman gods, goddesses, soldiers, statesmen and poets. Palladian villas and temples had spread over the English landscape. The young Duke of Devonshire at Chatsworth, Lord Lansdowne at Bowood, the Duke of Bedford at Woburn, the Prince Regent at Carlton House and now the Duke of Wellington at Apsley House and Strathfieldsaye were buying antique statues or copies imported from Italy. The fashion reached its height with the sensational importation of the marbles from the Parthenon at Athens by the Earl of Elgin. These marbles, conveyed to England eight years earlier, had cost Lord Elgin £74,000. He offered them to the nation for £35,000. Immediately a controversy raged. Should they have been removed from the Acropolis? Were they the work of Phidias? Were they worth the money? Byron inveighed against their removal as vandalism. A haggard Athena appeared to the poet and denounced the rape of her monuments—

> *She ceased awhile and thus I dared reply,*
> *To soothe the vengeance kindling in her eye:*
> *"Daughter of Jove! in Britain's injured name,*
> *A true-born Briton may the deed disclaim.*
> *Frown not on England; England owns him not:*
> *Athena, No! Thy plunderer was a Scot!"*

The marbles were put on view at Lord Elgin's house on the corner of Park Lane and Piccadilly, and there the crowd flocked while art critics, connoisseurs and politicians joined in the battle. The House of Commons appointed a committee to hold a hearing and summoned to it Sir Thomas Lawrence, Benjamin West, Flaxman, Nollekens, Westmacott, Chantrey and other giants of the art world. It was the great Canova's opinion that clinched the argument. Invited to England to express his views, he declared that the marbles were undoubtedly genuine works of Phidias, that their removal contributed to their preservation, that the price asked by the noble lord was modest. So the nation bought them and they went into the British Museum.

Fêted, the Marquis Canova returned to Rome. He was one of its greatest figures. Every distinguished man, every great lady who went to see the Roman Forum, the Coliseum and St Peter's went to see Canova's studio.

Severn called on the great man. Shy and full of trepidation, he was received with much cordiality by the sculptor, who took him through the workshops and showed him the work in hand. He saw in creation *Mars and Venus*, and *The Three Graces*, the latter commissioned at a price of three thousand guineas by the Prince Regent. As a compliment, the Prince's portrait had been carved upon the shield of Mars. There was a statue of Napoleon, a work for the Duke of Wellington, who, having sent him to St Helena, would now exhibit his effigy in his new Apsley House. There was a bust of Napoleon's mother, Madame Mère, and another of the Emperor's faithless wife, Marie Louise, mother of the little King of Rome, now reigning at Parma with her paramour, the Grand Master of the Court, the one-eyed General Neipperg.

"I have done almost all of the Emperor's family, some thirty-six busts—so I know them pretty well," said Canova. He stopped before the lovely head of a small boy. "That's the Duke of Reichstadt—King of Rome." He paused, smoothed the cheek with his hand and said, "Poor little boy!" The tour concluded, Canova took Severn back to the simple house where he lived with his Abbé brother, and there, over a glass of wine and amid the fumes of tobacco, talked of England, Paris, Napoleon and the great figures he had known. Before his enchanted young guest departed he promised to send a letter to the Pope requesting permission for him to study in any of the Vatican galleries.

Almost dizzy with ecstasy after the great man's reception of him, Severn left the narrow side-street with the studio door to which kings and queens and princes had flocked. A few paces and he found himself in the busy Corso, near the house where Goethe had lived. In Rome he was indeed among the immortals. With a head full of ambitious dreams, flushed, hat in hand, his dark chestnut curls tumbling over his brow, he strode triumphantly along. What a story he would have for Keats, who had urged him to make the call despite his diffidence!

At that moment an open carriage drawn by a pair of light bays came down the Corso. In it sat a lady with two young girls. They were unmistakably English and aristocratic in bearing. Their eyes fell on the happy young man, who gave them a radiant glance.

"I wonder who he is!" said one of the girls eagerly.

"I suspect he's just come out of Canova's studio—an Italian model," replied her sister Julia.

"He's English—very English, with that complexion and hair," said Mrs Walker, their mother. "I should say he's a student, not a model. He's certainly a remarkable young man."

"Oh we must find out who he is!" said the elder girl, Maria, a pretty blonde of twenty-one.

"I generally find that people who look remarkable are quite ordinary when you come to know them. Rome's a small place. Somebody always knows somebody here, so I've no doubt, Maria, you'll find out who he is," said Mrs Walker teasingly.

Certainly there were other remarkable young men in Rome among the foreign colony. The students of painting mostly went to Florence; those of sculpture came to Rome, for it had not only the attraction of Canova, now ageing, but of Thorwaldsen, the Dane on whose shoulders Canova's mantle seemed likely to fall. He also enjoyed an international reputation. Celebrities flocked to his studio in the Via Sistina. Three years ago, Byron, visiting Rome, had sat for him, and was not wholly pleased with the result. "It doesn't resemble me at all. I look much more unhappy," he complained. Byron had stayed in the Piazza di Spagna, almost opposite the house where Severn and Keats now lived. He had grumbled at the number of English in Rome that stared at him. Society was indeed present in force. There were enough peers with their coroneted carriages in the Piazza to make a House of Lords. Thorwaldsen had no complaint about this. They were good patrons. They bought lavishly. He had a big studio with workmen knocking out his designs. Lord Ruthven, who had called on him that morning, found him finishing works for the Duke of Bedford, Lord Lucan and Prince Leopold.

In such an atmosphere, mused Severn, going homewards with a singing heart, how could he fail to scale the heights? He was twenty-six, his ambition was illimitable. Had not the young Canova arrived unknown in Rome with only a pension of a few pounds from the Venetian Republic? Now he was one of the great figures of Europe, the friend of kings and Popes. Yes, he would win that Academy pension and then he could stay on in Rome, he and John Keats. Together they would win fame, as others before them.

He turned from the Corso into the Via Condotti, leading up to the Piazza di Spagna. Above him, golden in the evening sunlight gilding its façade, stood the Church of the Trinità crowning the great flight of steps. On the corner of the Piazza, before he crossed to their house, there was an old man with a stall of books. He stopped to glance over them. There was nothing in English, but he found a small volume of poems by Alfieri. He bought it, knowing it would give Keats pleasure. They were both

c

struggling with Italian. Keats was far ahead of him and could now read it with little difficulty. Almost at their door, on another stall, he bought some flowers. They were December roses, and cheap, but it was a great extravagance nevertheless. Their scanty funds had rapidly diminished. Keats's publisher, Taylor, had generously given him one hundred pounds for the copyright of *Endymion*, and he himself from miniatures he had painted had raised almost fifty pounds. They had now been three months out of England. Their funds were so low that, unknown to Keats, he had sent home an appeal to his friends. The nights grew longer and colder. They needed fuel. Dr Clark, unwearying, helpful, had as yet presented no bill. Severn tried hard to conceal from Keats that with housework and attending upon him, other distractions apart, his picture progressed but slowly. If he did not win the Academy Scholarship, what would happen to them?

There was another person buying flowers, a fashionably dressed elderly Englishwoman. She bought a prodigious quantity. A carriage with liveried coachman and groom was drawn up by the kerb. She called to the groom, who jumped down from the boxseat and collected the flowers she had bought. A large bunch of roses fell on the pavement as he went to the carriage, following the lady. Severn retrieved it and she thanked him graciously.

"I can't resist buying roses—and in December!" she exclaimed in a lovely voice, smiling.

"Quite intoxicating, ma'am," he replied. "But so is everything in Rome."

She looked at him, struck by the sensitive beauty of the young man's face. He in turn noticed her grace and distinction. Everything about her, her dress, manners, the simple collar of pearls, the silk bonnet and shawl, denoted fashion and wealth.

"You are English of course? And newly in Rome?" she

asked pleasantly. Then seating herself in her carriage she gave an order to the coachman in Italian. Without waiting for Severn's response, she drove off, giving him a farewell smile.

His eyes followed the equipage until it had vanished. He stood holding his book and flowers, wondering who she was. To be able to buy a carriageful of flowers, to drive off to some beautiful palace with pictures and servants and never to have to reckon what anything you might fancy would cost! He had glimpsed a world that was not his, but being young, ambitious and optimistic, even while he wondered he felt no envy.

When Severn opened the door into the sitting-room he found Keats was not alone. Elton was there. They had come back from their afternoon ride along the Tiber. Keats was on the couch. At once the ghastly pallor of his face alarmed Severn. After a few minutes Elton departed. It was plain that he wished to say something to Severn, who followed him out through the landlady's room on to the narrow marble stairs.

"I don't think he should ride any more," said Elton quietly. "He had a frightful coughing fit as we came up the Via Babuino. We had to halt frequently. I've never seen him so bad as to-day. It exhausted him terribly."

"Then we'll stop it," answered Severn. "Come in and talk to him to-morrow—he always enjoys your company."

"Certainly. Then—till to-morrow."

He turned, went down a flight of steps, paused and looked up, addressing Severn, smiling.

"By the way, I think I might tell you—I'm well in favour with Princess Borghese!" he said, a little ring of triumph in his voice. "It was very simple and she was on to my manœuvre at once. The day before yesterday I was riding on the Pincio when her carriage came up abreast. We progressed side by side. I gave her a special bow. She smiled. As we moved along she remarked that it was *un bel giorno*. It was! At the end of the *viale* she stopped the carriage—and I halted too. We talked and she asked me to call. I went last evening. My reception was everything I could desire. I'm returning this evening!"

He looked up at Severn, elated. Then, seeing no response in Severn's face, "I surprise you?" he asked. "I'm sorry. My dear fellow, my days are numbered," he said, tapping his chest. "Don't begrudge me a little *divertimento*."

He smiled up at Severn, but there was more pathos than happiness in his smile. With a wave of the hand he went on down the steps.

II

There was no more riding. For a week the weather was unsettled and there was a threat of winter in the air. Then the sun shone again. Keats sat every noonday by his window looking down on the Steps, the water splashing in the fountain, the flower-sellers, the artists' models waiting to be hired, and all the animation of the Piazza. It was a pageant of moving colour in the bright air.

One day, Elton leaning out of their window called to them. A lady drove by in a crimson calèche. "Look, there's the Countess of Albany, Bonnie Prince Charlie's widow! She lives in Florence. She won't live here because the Pope doesn't recognise her as the Queen of England. I saw her brother-in-law, Henry, Cardinal Duke—the last of the Stuarts—buried here last year. He'd tried to stop her affair with Alfieri, but couldn't, and they went off and lived together in Florence. I hear she's got another lover now, a French painter."

They watched the carriage pass, and had a glimpse of an elderly woman swathed in furs.

"Canova's doing a monument of the Stuarts—old James and his two sons, for St Peter's. I wonder if she's

here to look at it. That would be very odd," said Elton.
"She commissioned Canova to do Alfieri's monument in
Santa Croce at Florence. When the Bishop objected to it
as a tribute to fornication, she got the Pope to overrule
him. The old Cardinal Duke's left her a legacy, they say.
What a woman!"

Two bishops in violet soutanes went by on their way to
the nearby College of Propaganda of the Faith. Then
came a bevy of scurrying young seminarists, some in
purple soutanes with black mantles and red belts, from
the Scots College, others in vivid scarlet, from the German and Hungarian colleges. There were monks in black
and brown habits, the papal police in blue uniforms with
gold epaulettes and tricorne hats, gallants in tight
lavender pantaloons, ladies in high-bodiced gowns,
beggars, English grooms, chestnut-vendors, and *pifferari*
who came in native costume from the Abruzzi mountains,
playing their bagpipes now that their sheep were in the
winter folds and they must turn an honest *soldo*. The
pageant was unending.

In the evenings when the shutters were closed and the
temperature fell, Severn and Keats retreated into the
small bedroom that had a fireplace. While Keats lay on
the bed reading, Severn worked on his picture *Alcibiades*
for the Academy travelling pension. All his future
depended on gaining it.

The little book of poems by Alfieri delighted Keats who
read it aloud, translating. One evening he abruptly
stopped when he had read—

> *Misera me! sollievo a me non resta*
> *Altro che'l pianto, ed il pianto è delitto*

Unhappy me! No comfort remains for me other than
weeping, and weeping is a crime.

His voice choked on the words, and he put down the

book. The passage struck at his heart. Doomed, he knew he could never fulfil his high ambitions. He would die with his best work unwritten.

He was sunk so deep in despair that nothing Severn could say relieved the misery of his soul. When his friend insisted that he was improving, he shook his head. To cover the terrible silence that fell between them Severn put down his brushes and went to the piano. He played the Haydn music that Keats loved, to prevent him from brooding on his fate. But it was in vain. Music failed him these days.

III

By the second week in December Keats was too listless to go out. He could keep no food in his stomach. There was a morning when he could not rise, shaken by paroxysms of coughing. He vomited a great quantity of blood. Dr Clark was sent for and took from his arm eight ounces to relieve the congestion. When he had gone Keats suddenly leapt from his bed vowing that that day should be his last. After a frightful scene Severn got him back into his bed. For five nights and days Keats seemed never to sleep. Severn watched by his bedside, dozing in a chair. It did not seem possible that the racked body could hold life much longer, with no food retained, with vomiting and incessant cold sweats. His mind was now in as desperate a state as his body. He craved death. He had come out from England with some laudanum. He declared that he would encompass his end with it, having given up all hope of recovery.

He asked for the laudanum, but Severn had hidden it away. There was a violent scene in which Keats demanded it as his rightful property. He would not suffer a lingering death. But Severn was obdurate and neither the force nor the pathos of Keats's appeal shook his denial. The rage

passed and the poet lay silent and exhausted. The next day
Dr Clark took the laudanum away with him.

Day after day the dreadful ordeal continued. Christmas
and the New Year came. With incessant care Severn
nursed his dying friend. Sometimes he carried him into
the adjacent room while he changed the stained bed linen.
He battled with his own despair. Their money was running out. A visit to Torlonia's had been in vain. The bank
would not accept a promissory note. Dr Clark, though
well aware that his bill would never be met, was ceaseless
in his attention. A new threat descended upon them in the
form of the horrible landlady. For now the truth could
no longer be disguised. Under Roman law, should a
lodger die of contagious disease, the furniture, beds and
curtains must be burnt and the walls scraped, all at the
cost of the occupant. Signora Angeletti had gone to the
police and reported that one of her lodgers was dying of
consumption. From her apartment she kept a hostile
watch. She raised no finger to help.

Elton came to see them, bringing flowers and books.
Sometimes he sat by Keats, while Severn, utterly exhausted by his nightly vigil, slept in the adjacent room.
Elton and the doctor were their only contacts in Rome.
They were so terribly alone and so far removed from those
who knew them and cared for them. When Severn wrote
to Keats's friends, to the Brawnes, to Taylor and Brown,
and to his own family, he was so tired and distraught that
tears came to his eyes and he could hardly see what he
was writing.

IV

Beyond the windows of that house where an unknown
young English poet of genius was slowly dying in deep
despair the life of Rome went on, vivacious in its multi-
tudinous activities. Down in the Roman Forum the hired

prisoners from the Papal jails were bringing to light the lost monuments of ancient Rome. This was being done at the expense of the Duchess of Devonshire, who, by virtue of rank, wealth and talents, was the recognised leader of English society. Her close friendship with Cardinal Consalvi, Pius VII's confidant and Secretary of State, provided baseless gossip, but gossip was the life-blood of Roman society.

The widowed Duchess had been the second wife of the fifth Duke of Devonshire when she married him in 1809, and a lifelong friend of the first Duchess, the celebrated Georgiana, whose beauty had been immortalised by Gainsborough and Reynolds. The two ladies had lived together for some time in the ducal household. They had not escaped the accusation that it was a *ménage-à-trois*. The Duke's household was somewhat peculiar. His legitimate and illegitimate children all grew up together and there were the strangest rumours afloat.

The second Duchess came of eccentric stock. Her father was the Bishop of Derry and Earl of Bristol. He had gallivanted all over Europe with a vast retinue of servants and coaches. She had first married a man named Foster. On his death she joined her friend Georgiana and the Duke. The two ladies, both of remarkable beauty and talents, wrote and painted and kept a small salon in Lausanne. It was here that Lady Elizabeth Foster had overwhelmed by her beauty and intelligence a stout little man who had just completed, after years of prodigious labour, a historical work. He took much pleasure in reading his manuscript to her. A pernickety little bachelor of fifty, one day he went down on his knees in a proposal of marriage. In a tribute he had written he compared Lady Elizabeth with the Duchess Georgiana: "Bess is much nearer the level of a mortal, but a mortal for whom the wisest man, historic or medical, would throw away two or three worlds if he had them in possession. . . . If she chose to beckon the Lord Chancellor from his wool-sack in full sight of the world he would not resist obedi-ence." It was pleasant to be admired, to have Mr Gibbon, the author of the *Decline and Fall of the Roman Empire*, on his knees before her, but kneeling or standing he was not a figure of romance, being short and portly. So she declined his offer graciously and their friendship regained its sensible basis.

Following the death of her friend Georgiana, Lady Elizabeth married the widowed Duke and thus became the Duchess of Devonshire. The Duke died five years later, whereupon she took up residence in Rome. By rank and personality she dominated the large English colony, and was equally popular with the Roman aristocracy. Her intellectual gifts were considerable. She printed editions-de-luxe of Virgil and Horace. Caught in the current craze for excavation, she lavishly endowed exploration of the Roman Forum, which lay thirty feet below the meadows where cows now pastured among the columns of ancient temples. The living as well as the dead interested her. Canova, Thorwaldsen, Consalvi and the leading figures of Roman society thronged the salons of the palace where she entertained.

She was capricious in her choice of guests and inclined to be censorious. Although she enjoyed a close friendship with the Duc de Laval-Montmorency, French Ambas-sador to the Holy See, she regarded the Princess Pauline Borghese with distaste. She deplored the weak patriotism of such Englishmen as Lord Lansdowne, Lord Jersey, Lord Cowper, Lord Henry Russell and Mr Brougham the politician, who flocked to the Princess's palazzo and seemed entranced by her raffish company. She could admire the Pope for generously offering the Bonaparte clan an asylum in Rome, but she wished that her countrymen

would show a little less eagerness to be the guests of
the notorious Princess. Napoleon was still a prisoner in
St Helena and Waterloo was only five years away. If
Lady Holland liked to make herself ridiculous with her
pro-Bonapartism, the Duchess felt that it was even more
necessary in a city swarming with the pinchbeck ex-kings
and princes of a fallen Empire for her to show a proper
sense of patriotism. She was somewhat cool, therefore,
when one day, halting her carriage to greet a young
American, Mr Ticknor, she was told by him that he was
going to a party to be given that evening by the Princess
Borghese, where he hoped to see Her Grace.

"No. I shall not be there, Mr Ticknor. You will appreciate that some of us British do not feel attracted by the
Bonapartes. With an American, of course, it is different.
I hope I shall see you on Thursday. You were a very great
success at my dinner last Tuesday with Lady Westmorland
who asked if you were coming."

"Thank you, Duchess. I am looking forward to
Thursday."

She smiled at him and gave the word to her coachman.
The carriage went on. He stood, hat in hand, conscious
that he had unwittingly blundered. But how could he
know all the cross-currents in this city, a hotbed of
intrigues, political, social, ecclesiastical? He liked the
Duchess of Devonshire and it thrilled him to be a guest at
her table. Her palazzo was a great exchange to which the
whole world came.

A graduate of Harvard, twenty-eight, wealthy, Ticknor
had set forth four years ago to see the Old World, the
forerunner of a great host of his countrymen who were to
explore post-Napoleonic Europe. Luck had favoured him
throughout. Eager, with youth's fresh charm, well-
mannered and handsome, his sensitive nose scented genius
wherever it could be found. In the space of four years it

had carried him far, and he had made a nice collection of celebrities—Chateaubriand, Goethe, Metternich, Mme de Staël, Talleyrand and Wordsworth. He had met the fabulous Byron in Venice. His quick mind and ingenious manner captivated the moody lord, who had received him with much cordiality. He gave him an autographed copy of his poems and, hearing he was about to visit Greece and the Morea, sent him away with a letter of introduction to Ali Pasha, the bloodthirsty old Turk who had settled himself at Janina in the rôle of bandit-sultan whom none of the Powers could tame. And now here he was in Rome again with a diary full of notable happenings and a head full of plans. Having discarded law for the moment, he would be content to become the President of the United States, or at least Secretary of State. Or better, he would win fame as a writer, but what he would write he could not yet determine.

CHAPTER III

I

FEBRUARY came. In the house on the Spanish steps the grim drama progressed. Keats grew a little more composed. His pallor was ghastly, his cheeks sunken, but the glowing life of his hazel eyes was unabated. From time to time he aroused himself from the coma into which he was sinking. "Severn," he said one day with a smile that wrung his friend's heart, "I bequeath to you all the joy and prosperity I have never had. It would be a second death for me if I knew that your goodness now was your loss hereafter."

In more conscious moments he expressed his distress at his lingering illness. He was deeply worried by the thought that he was taking from Severn the time he should be devoting to the Academy picture. In that little narrow bedroom with its blue-raftered ceiling, brown-tiled floor and windows through which in the daytime came the sound of carriages in the Piazza and of feet mounting the Steps, he lay waiting for death. "How long is this posthumous life of mine to last?" he asked Dr Clark one day. A medical student, they could hide nothing from him. He warned Severn of the progressive stages through which he must pass before the end.

He had no faith to sustain him, but he made no objections when Severn, steadfast in his own Christian belief, prayed by his bedside. One day he said: "My dear Severn —here am I with a desperation in death that would disgrace the commonest fellow. If you could get me some of the works of Jeremy Taylor to read from to me, I might become really a Christian and leave this world in peace."

So Severn got *Holy Living and Dying* and read from it.

But it availed little. His mind had dwelt for years in another world. Endymion had been his companion and those immortal youths and maidens of a far Grecian day, who moved "forever young, forever fair." To Pilate's question, "What is truth?" he had answered with the lyrical ecstasy of adolescence—"Beauty is Truth, Truth Beauty, that is all ye know on earth and all ye need to know."

There had been an occasion when Severn had unwittingly touched the core of his misery. Letters came from England which Severn read to him. He listened, and once he said, "What they say seems no longer to concern me. I have already journeyed far beyond them." He mourned every circumstance of his past life, the lost happiness, the frustration of his love. One letter, given to him by Severn in the belief that it came from one of their friends, proved to be from Fanny Brawne. He gave one glance at the handwriting and put it down unopened, torn with the passion that the sight of it evoked. He asked Severn to put it in his coffin along with a purse of his sister's and a letter with some hair; then, later, vacillating in his distress, he asked that it should not be put there.

There came a day when Keats inquired about the place of burial. Severn promised to go and inspect the piece of ground by the Porta San Paolo to which the Protestants were consigned. He chose a sunny day when the English nurse Dr Clark had found for them came in. He was dropping with lack of sleep and nervous prostration, but he made the journey across Rome, with Elton, to the little wilderness by the ancient pyramid-tomb of Caius Cestius and the Aurelian Wall. It was in a fashion a place of exile in the meadows frequented by the Romans on holidays. Wild flowers grew there, violets, daisies, anemones, and funereal cypresses, dark sentinels against the sky. Severn brought back a few flowers he had picked among those pathetic graves of the dead in exile. A young shepherd and flock of sheep and goats had given it a Theocritean air. He faithfully described the place to Keats, whose eyes rested on the flowers. Among them were some violets, which he loved above all others. He was glad to learn they flourished amid the graves. "Already I seem to feel them growing over me," he said.

Later the nurse failed them and Elton suddenly disappeared, but they were visited by Ewing, an English friend of Elton's, a young sculptor. Night after night Severn kept his vigil by Keats's bed. Sometimes he wrote letters, sometimes he drew to pass the time. One morning about 3 a.m. he made a sketch of Keats. "Drawn to keep me awake—a deadly sweat was on him all this night," he wrote at the bottom of it. He kept his family posted, consumed with homesickness. How friendly and warm seemed that little home in Shoreditch! He had brought with him a miniature he had made of his father and mother, his three vivacious sisters and his two younger brothers. Despite their father's violent temper, they were a devoted circle, painting and music their constant interest. Severn feasted his eyes on the picture.

They had reached the second week of February. The doctor had told Severn that there was no hope and the end could not be far off. A great calm had come over Keats, who was so weak that he lay scarcely conscious but he had lucid intervals. He warned Severn of the nature of his end, his eyes still bright in his emaciated face.

He woke one evening, and in the calmest manner, out of the bitterness of his heart, moved by the hopelessness of his fate, asked Severn to place over his resting-place the words *Here lies one whose name was writ in water*. "If I had had time I would have made myself remembered. But not now," he said, sadly.

For two more days he lingered, and then on a Friday

afternoon the death-throes began. Severn was alone with him.

"Lift me up for I am dying. I shall die easy. Don't be frightened! Thank God it has come," said Keats. "The letter from Fanny—don't open it, put it with me, over my heart, Severn."

"Everything you wish—everything shall be done," replied Severn.

Even now the end was delayed. The evening light faded from the sky, the twittering of the starlings round the houses ceased. Severn lit the candles. There was no one to go across the Piazza for the doctor. It did not matter. Keats was beyond all human aid. It was ten o'clock when he sank into a calm that might have been sleep or death. Severn did not move, and sat in the silence of the dimly lit room. He had never seen death before but after two months of such suffering he could not mourn for this release. Keats was receding quietly from life. About eleven o'clock there was no labouring of breath. He bent over his friend, scarcely knowing whether he slept or had gone. He brought a candle from the table and held it close to Keats's face and found there the sleep of eternity.

He put back the candle and drew up the sheet. Then he went to the window, opened it and stood looking up at the starry sky. It was the twenty-third of February, 1821. He was too exhausted for tears. For nine nights he had never left the bedside of his friend. For four months he had professed a false hope and had opposed the deep despair of a man who felt that life had cheated him of health, love and happiness. And yet what richness glowed in that tortured soul, what music it had given them as a hostage to Time!

He turned from the window, closed the door of the death-chamber and went into his own room. Then for the first time in all those terrible weeks he burst into tears.

Half an hour later, calmer, he went back and prayed beside the bed of his dead friend, after which he rose, put on a greatcoat, for the night was chilly, and went across the Piazza to inform Dr Clark. The clocks were striking midnight over sleeping Rome.

II

On Monday they buried John Keats. The little procession consisted of only two carriages. There were so few to mourn him. They moved away from the house in the Piazza di Spagna while the darkness of night lay over it. It was not safe for a Protestant funeral to pass through the streets of Rome in daylight. So detested were these foreigners outside the grace of the Holy Church that a police guard had to be mounted over the cemetery to prevent the desecration of the graves. For this reason the authorities insisted on interments in the Cemetery of the Acattolici, as it was called, by torchlight or not later than dawn.

The light was breaking when the carriages halted by the Pyramid of Caius Cestius and the small procession followed the coffin across the grassy meadow. They came to an open grave in the far corner, a little apart from a cluster of headstones gleaming coldly in the breaking light. Severn, scarcely able to walk from exhaustion, was assisted by William Ewing, who had come through the darkness to his rooms and had helped him to dress and go down into the carriage. He now stood by the grave's brink supporting Severn while an English clergyman, a stranger to him, read the burial service in the still dawn. Severn thought of his friends in England, of those who had loved the dead man. He was the only one of that youthful, happy circle to be present at this farewell. Only three persons here, Dr Clark, Ewing and himself, had known the living poet, and he solely in all the ardour of his genius in those memorable days when they had gathered in Leigh Hunt's home in the Vale of Hampstead, or debated around Charles Brown's fireside. There were seven persons by the graveside all told: the English chaplain, Dr Clark, Ewing, Seymour Kirkup, a friend of Ewing's, and two others of the English Colony in Rome, and all except two were unknown to him.

The earth rattled on the coffin and as the last solemn words "Ashes to ashes, dust to dust" were pronounced the sun came up over the horizon. The cypresses stood black against the break of day. On the tomb of Caius Cestius, seen by St Paul on his way to execution beyond the city gates, the light brought colour to the weathered marble. It spread over the crumbling, bastioned wall built by the Emperor Aurelianus to fortify Rome against the barbarians, and lit the daisied grass.

Then they turned away leaving an English poet to his long sleep.

III

A week after the funeral, recovered from his exhaustion, Severn took stock of his circumstances. He had a bill for the stripping and fumigation of their dwelling, for the funeral of Keats and for the doctor who had nobly assisted him through these harrowing months. It transpired that his promissory note had been rejected in error by Torlonia's bank, and he now had this money in hand, but after all the expenses had been met he would be reduced to only a few pounds. Should he remain in Rome or return to England? The painting that he wished to submit in the competition for the award of the Royal Academy's travelling pension was in a preliminary stage. Despite all poor Keats's urging, it had not been possible to progress with it. The painting must be despatched by July at the latest for the Academy Council. His theme was a classical one, *The*

Death of Alcibiades. Thus far he had only roughly sketched it in charcoal. If he remained here in Rome, he must earn money until his picture received the award, should it be successful. His present asset was an ability to paint miniatures. Two years ago he had painted one of Keats, and to their delight it had been hung in the Royal Academy Exhibition. With it went his first painting. They were both badly hung, but at least they had been accepted.

He remembered so well making that miniature of his lost friend. It was May and the nightingales were singing in the garden at Wentworth Place, where Keats was living with their friend, Charles Brown. To that double house the Brawnes had come as neighbours, the mother, and the daughter Fanny who had captured Keats's heart. Keats's love story had just begun, she eighteen, he twenty-three and in the high flood of his creative genius. There in the garden at Wentworth Place, on a day early in May, where he had come for a sitting, Severn had found Keats lying under a plum tree, hands folded behind his head, in an ecstatic trance as he listened to a nightingale pouring forth its song. He remembered this occasion clearly because a few days later Keats had read to Brown and himself from scraps of paper his *Ode to a Nightingale.* He remembered also how he surmised that some of the lines were autobiographical—

> *Fade far away, dissolve and quite forget*
> *What thou among the leaves hast never known,*
> *The weariness, the fever and the fret*
> *Here where men sit and hear each other groan.*

Tom, Keats's beloved young brother, had died in his arms six months earlier after devoted nursing—died of the same disease that in turn had struck down Keats.

Severn went into the small bedroom of his apartment and opened the shutters, letting in the morning light. He had been away from it for a week—a week of complete rest, of unbroken sleep and kind attention. After the funeral Dr Clark, Ewing, and his friend Seymour Kirkup had come back with him. They would not let him stay alone in a place of such sad memories. Nervously exhausted, he was on the verge of a breakdown. Unable to eat or sleep, tied to his vigil in the small bedroom, he had grown pale and emaciated. Dr Clark, alarmed at his state, had called in a nurse. For a whole week he had been kept in bed.

After a few days Ewing and Kirkup discussed the situation with him. They were strongly opposed to his remaining at 26 Piazza di Spagna. Kirkup had a friend who was leaving Rome. He had a small studio in the Via San Isidoro, opposite the former convent of the Irish fathers. The rent was less than Severn was paying now. They had been to see it, on the second floor up a broad flight of stone steps. It was a studio and bedroom with a north light, sparsely furnished, the property of the outgoing tenant, a young Danish sculptor who had been studying under Thorwaldsen. He asked a modest sum to which Severn had agreed.

It was his last day in the old rooms in the Piazza di Spagna. As he opened the shutters and the beauty of Rome lay before him he was blinded with tears at the thought of his vanished friend who had spent so many hours at this window. In these last weeks he had grown conscious of something that youth in its intoxication rarely apprehends, the mystery of human existence, its brevity, its helplessness in the presence of inscrutable Fate. His faith, hitherto unchallenged, had known no doubts, no misgivings. But his friend, gentle and sweet in character, a spirit of such sensitivity that he had been one with the beauty of flowers, the songs of birds, the splendour of sunrise and sunset, had vanished, having bequeathed to a world that had given him nothing but anguish and pain, a legacy it scarcely heeded. He had died in pagan loneliness, and yet if virtue knew a resurrection would he not inherit the kingdom of all choice spirits? Would a merciful God shut out this gifted soul who had suffered and sung amongst them here on earth?

Conscious of an unfathomable mystery, Severn stood by the window in a trance of thought until the jangle of the noonday bells broke over Rome. Then he turned away, briefly surveying the silent room, weighed down by the almost unbearable memories it evoked. Yet even in this hour of pain he was conscious how all his future years would seem enriched by this harrowing experience.

IV

Within three months there came an incredible change in his life. He was happy in his work in the little studio. He found himself in the centre of a small artistic colony. At the end of the street, terminating in a long flight of steps, stood the Church of San Isidoro with its baroque façade. Adjoining it there was a convent and a large garden with cypresses, eucalyptus and pine trees. The church was built for the Irish Franciscan monks, but Napoleon, descending on Rome, had scattered them. The convent, now somewhat derelict, had been taken over as a lodging by a group of poor artists, mostly Germans. Its leader was a man of thirty-two, Johann Overbeck. He had been living in Rome for a dozen years after studying under the great David. Living here with a number of his countrymen, all poor and enthusiastic, they turned the convent into a warren of art. In revolt against the classical Renaissance and its sensuousness, they laid the foundation of a Nazarene school that invoked much derision. Tenacious in their cheerful poverty, they maintained their theory of art against all critics. Overbeck, though young, was well on the road to success. He had decorated the house of the Prussian Consul and had painted three large frescoes in the villa of Prince Massimo. Severn met him one day by accident in a little inn they both frequented at lunchtime, where Overbeck took some of the Chianti in his neighbour's flask. Apologising for his error, they got into conversation and Overbeck invited him to visit his studio. From that time onwards Severn ran in and out of the convent visiting its bohemian occupants, who in turn frequented his studio. They conversed excitedly on all matters in a frightful mixture of German, English and Italian. Their debates were long and passionate, but were conducted with much good humour, though Severn sturdily defended the classical school that was anathema to these "Nazarites," as they were nicknamed because of their addiction to Biblical characters and themes.

It was to Overbeck that Severn owed his introduction to the Bunsens, who lived in the Palazzo Caffarelli which stood high up on a bluff of the Capitol. The windows of its rooms, above a garden full of orange and ilex trees, had one of the finest prospects in Rome. The Palazzo looked down on the whole of the Roman Forum with its columns and ruined temples, at the end of which appeared the great amphitheatre of the Coliseum. In the far distance rose Monte Cava on the violet horizon, with Rocca di Papa clinging like a swallow's nest to the mountain side. Eastwards could be discerned Frascati, the little town with the fabulous villas of the Roman Princes.

Mrs Bunsen was a young Englishwoman who had married Charles Bunsen, Secretary of the Prussian Legation. Their marriage had been a Roman romance. Six years earlier a Mr and Mrs Waddington had arrived in Rome with their three daughters to spend the season. They rented the first floor of the Palazzo Gavotti. Their pretty and accomplished young daughters soon became popular in society. Mr Waddington, of a studious nature, was almost a recluse, but his wife entertained constantly. To one of her receptions came young Charles Bunsen, employed at the Prussian Legation. He worked under its Envoy to Rome, Georg Niebuhr, who, as well as being a diplomat, already had a considerable reputation as a historian.

Young Bunsen, with his handsome presence and agreeable manners, soon became a welcome visitor at the Palazzo Gavotti. The eldest sister having become engaged, Frances, the younger sister, found herself receiving attentions from Charles Bunsen. They had congenial interests; both being of studious disposition, they visited the Roman ruins and made wider excursions in the Campagna. They began to read German together. By the spring of 1817 they knew they were falling in love, the penniless German student with the wealthy English girl. April passed and on a morning in May, shortly before the Waddingtons' departure for England, young Charles, in agony at the impending separation, poured out the story of his love for Frances to the astonished Mrs Waddington, who had never suspected the true state of affairs. Mr Waddington, hearing of this, alarmed, consulted the young man's chief, whereupon Mr Niebuhr without hesitation said, "The talent, abilities and character of Charles Bunsen are a capital more safely to be reckoned upon than any other, however securely invested, and had I a daughter myself, to such a man I would gladly consign her." With this recommendation the Waddingtons felt that true love might take its course.

That same evening Charles Bunsen and Frances Waddington made an excursion to the Coliseum to view it in moonlight. The centre of the vast amphitheatre was occupied by a giant cross marking the place in the arena where so many had suffered martyrdom for the Christian faith. It was a scene of emotional beauty, and here by the steps of the cross, at eleven o'clock on the night of Saturday, May 31st, 1817, Charles Bunsen asked Frances Waddington to become his wife.

They were married one month later in the ancient chapel of the Palazzo Savelli built upon the ruins of the theatre of Marcellus. The honeymoon was spent at Frascati in the Casino Accoramboni, a half-villa, half-farmhouse with an old garden, a lost paradise with a view of Rome across the Campagna. Thus began a life of unbroken devotion.

Their honeymoon was idyllic in its setting. They spent long summer days among the wooded hills above the wide Campagna, they rowed on the lakes of Albano and Nemi, azure gems deeply framed in precipitous woods. They read Dante and Milton to the tinkle of fountains in the terraced gardens of the villa. They lived and slept in the great, frescoed rooms with high, painted ceilings. The days were radiant under an azure heaven, the nights cool and velvety, spangled with stars above the black cypresses, following a sunset of crimson and gold that bathed the plain and distant Rome in a fading glory. The dusk brought the fireflies dancing over the aromatic garden. In the early autumn they went back to Rome. Good fortune was with them. The position of Secretary to the Prussian Legation became vacant, and Bunsen was appointed.

They had been visited at Frascati by Overbeck, who brought with him his easel and paint-box. Mrs Bunsen, a talented amateur, spent enchanted hours painting with him while her husband read to them. Sometime after their return to Rome they moved into the Palazzo Caffarelli. There they kept open house for their friends, among them Overbeck and the local colony of German artists. Thorwaldsen the sculptor, working on a series of designs

from the *Iliad* and *Odyssey* for the Crown Prince of
Bavaria, recently in Rome, brought his pupils to the
palazzo. The Bunsens were musical, and the company of
young diplomats, painters and sculptors was augmented
by musicians who sang or played on the 'cello, flute,
piano and violin.

It was to the home of this friendly young couple that
Overbeck brought Severn. Mrs Bunsen welcomed him
warmly. She had heard the story of the death of Keats
and was filled with sorrow that she had not known of the
lonely ordeal of her two countrymen. Severn's bright and
affectionate personality at once established him in the
household, one of serious study and sober amusement. It
was the Bunsens who took him one evening in March to
the home of Georg Niebuhr.

A Danish civil servant, he had entered the service of
Prussia at the invitation of Baron Stein, the minister
who laid the foundations of Prussia, and who by uniting
the opposition to Napoleon after the battle of Leipzig,
had powerfully contributed to his downfall. Baron
Stein had been quick to see the qualities of young
Niebuhr, who had studied in London and Edinburgh. A
fine scholar, he had mastered twenty languages before he
was thirty. At the early age of thirty-six he had already
established himself as one of the most original of modern
historians by his lectures on Roman history. With this
background, Niebuhr had come in 1816 to his post in
Rome, a vigorous man of forty. He soon assumed a leading
position in the diplomatic corps.

The reception to which Severn and Overbeck were
taken by the Bunsens was given at the Palazzo Savelli,
where the Niebuhrs lived. It was in honour of Baron Stein
and Prince Hardenburg, the Prussian Prime Minister.
Royalty was present in the persons of the Prince and
Princess of Denmark. There was a company of about

three hundred, including the French and Austrian Ambassadors and the most notable figures of the Roman aristocracy. It was the first pageant of Roman life which Severn had seen and he was overcome by the brilliance and colour of the scene, the women blazing with diamonds the men almost gaudy with stars, jewels and sashes.

The arrival of the Bunsens with Overbeck and Severn coincided with a spectacular ceremonial at the foot of the great staircase. A large coach drew up and from it descended an old man in the crimson cape of a Cardinal, with red stockings and gold buckles on his shoes. He had a sallow face with sharp, glittering eyes. His close-cropped white head was surmounted by a small crimson cap. He made the sign of benediction to some of the crowd about the door who fell to their knees, among them Overbeck, who had embraced the Catholic faith. Instantly, as the Cardinal approached the great staircase, two footmen in livery appeared, carrying aloft large candelabra with lit candles. Ceremoniously carrying these, the recognised symbols of a Cardinal's reception, they preceded him up the flight of steps.

It was a ceremony of impressive beauty and it gained in interest when Severn was told the name of the Cardinal, a figure renowned in Rome who had played a singular rôle in recent history. He was Cardinal Fesch, the uncle of Napoleon and now the faithful companion of the Emperor's mother, Madame Mère, in the Palazzo Bonaparte, the palace with the glassed-in balcony on the corner of the Corso and the Piazza di Venezia.

The career of Cardinal Fesch had followed the rise and fall of the Empire. Gossip embellished with scurrilous details the story of the Cardinal's ascent from obscurity and poverty to eminence and wealth. Born in Corsica, the half-brother of Napoleon's mother, he entered the Church and might have lived all his life as a humble village curé had he not been the uncle of Napoleon. The outbreak of the French Revolution saw him appointed as storekeeper to the Army of the Alps. In this rôle he made a fortune by selling loot from Italy. When the First Consul decided on the restoration of Catholic worship, banned in France, it was easy, as part of the price of the Concordat with Pope Pius VII, to extract from him a biretta for Uncle Fesch. The ex-seminarist resumed the clerical habit and swiftly became in turn Archbishop of Lyons, Cardinal, and then French Ambassador to the Papal Court. Cardinal Fesch had shown a Bonaparte passion for loot but he had a loyalty to his Church that eventually brought him into conflict with his all-powerful nephew. When the Catholic clergy held a national conference in Paris he addressed them in words that seemed to censure Napoleon. He endorsed his independence by writing a letter of condolence to Pius VII, whom Napoleon was then holding in captivity at Fontainebleau. This indiscreet missive was intercepted. The Cardinal was banished to Lyons. Here he had lived until the approach of the Austrians in 1814, when he fled to Rome and joined Madame Mère. Since she was almost a recluse in her palazzo, Uncle Fesch, as he was known by the large Bonaparte clan in Rome, became chief representative of the family, and by virtue of his position as a Prince of the Church took precedence of all Napoleon's relatives, the ex-kings, queens, princes and princesses of his puppet kingdoms.

After the reception in the first salon of the Palazzo Savelli, the company moved into the long gallery, whose windows opened on to an enclosed garden containing fountains, orange trees and a vine pergola, all illuminated. It was a surprising garden, for the Niebuhrs' apartment was reached up a steep flight of seventy-three steps and was built over a colonnade of Ionic pillars that formed the third story of the ancient theatre of Marcellus. In the chapel of this palace, the property of Prince Orsini, the Bunsens had been married.

The large company having moved into the gallery, the music began. The choir from the Sistine Chapel, stationed on a dais at the end of the candle-lit gallery, sang Palestrina's *Mass for Pope Marcellus*, the motet *Tu es Petrus* and the *Dies Iræ* of Pittoni. They were unaccompanied, and their voices rose in melting harmonies under Peruzzi's magnificent painted ceiling. The sacred music performed, a quartet ascended the platform and played some music of Scarlatti's. But the event of the evening was the performance of the celebrated improvisatore, Signor Tommaso Sgricci. He was a stout middle-aged man whose fame had overrun Italy. He created dramas in lyrical verses on any theme suggested by the audience. These verses were delivered, extempore, to the accompaniment of the piano. Sgricci had rivals in this art, Signor Bondi and Signora Taddi, but he was easily their superior. Throughout the past winter all Rome had flocked to hear the famous improvisatore and although the smartest wits of the Roman salons had done their best to bring him down in defeat, he had triumphantly surmounted their tests. This evening he created a drama on the theme of Queen Christina's entry into Rome after her abdication of the Swedish Throne. The theme had been suggested by Baron von Reden, the Hanoverian Minister. It was a *tour de force* that provoked almost delirious applause. Although Severn had not sufficient Italian to appreciate the cleverness of the actor's verses, he was lost in admiration of the dramatic quality of this singular achievement.

When the concert ended, the company moved into another long salon used as a ballroom. It also opened on to the garden of orange trees. An orchestra began to play dance music. In a crowd by the door which had waited for the royalties to move into the ballroom, Severn ran into Kirkup, who greeted him and introduced him to a pretty blonde girl of about twenty, his cousin, Miss Carlow.

"Nancy's just arrived in Rome. She thinks she's in Paradise. Later she'll learn there's enough scandal and political villainy here to fit out a nice little hell," said Kirkup.

"I'm not going to let Seymour poison my paradise," declared Miss Carlow, laughing. "Have you been long in Rome, Mr Severn?"

"About five months."

"Aren't you the person who nursed the English poet who died here?"

"Yes—my friend John Keats," he answered.

How strange, he thought. He was to go through life as the man who had nursed a dying young English poet. It was becoming a legend in Rome. Few remembered the name of Keats, a poet who now seemed destined for immortality.

"Have I upset you?" asked Miss Carlow suddenly, noticing his expression. "Forgive me."

He made no answer, looking down at her lovely young face. The orchestra had begun to play a waltz.

"Can you waltz?" he asked abruptly.

"Yes—but not very well. I'm just learning it."

"Shall we?" he asking, putting out an arm. "I'm not very good at it myself." They moved into the dance.

Towards midnight he asked Miss Carlow for another dance, and when it was over they went out into the garden. Two cypresses rose up black and immense in the clear, starry sky. The air was perfumed by the scent of the orange blossom. The garden was full of guests sauntering and talking, the men imposing with their decorations, the women beautifully gowned and shining with jewels. The music from the ballroom drifted over them in the warm air. Severn was in a world that often took on the nature of a dream. How unreal it seemed to one who had been apprenticed at the age of fourteen to a London engraver, who had gone raw-boned and shabbily dressed to the Academy classes, who had lodged with his young married sister in Goswell Street five nights a week and gone to his home for the week-end, to live in the bosom of a family that played the piano, the violin, sang part-songs and somehow existed happily on the scanty earnings of an erratic, choleric and affectionate father. The girl now at his side reminded him of his sister Sarah. She had the same colouring, the same alert expression. Suddenly he began to tell her all about his brothers and sisters, his mother and father. They sat on in the garden until Seymour came and found them. The guests were leaving. Cardinal Fesch had gone home after the music. There could be no dancing until the Cardinal retired, so he had left, tactfully.

It was two o'clock when Severn mounted the stone steps to his studio in the Via San Isidoro. Kirkup had insisted on driving a party of eight back to his apartment, where they drank, ate and gossiped on his wide terrace overlooking the Villa Borghese. Severn's conscience troubled him a little. This was the third night in a week that he had been out until two o'clock. Social Rome was threatening the industry of a serious student.

CHAPTER IV

I

EVERY day the variety, vitality, and glamour of life in Rome, even for a poor artist, increased Severn's affection for the place. Whenever he went out into the streets on some mission he had to fight the temptation of a hundred sights. At the bottom of the street, with a convent and large garden, was the Church of Santa Maria della Concezione. The singular variety of its interests delighted Severn when one day Ewing took him in. It contained at the left of the high altar the tomb of Prince Alexander Sobieski, son of the King of Poland, and under the altar that of Cardinal Barberini, who had shown great hospitality to young John Milton during his visit to Rome in 1638; but it was not with the purpose of showing him these tombs that Ewing had drawn him aside. "If you wish to study anatomy, here is your chance!" he said. In four grottoes decorating its walls were the skulls of five hundred monks.

Severn had been installed in his new lodging for about a week when one morning Elton appeared. Nothing had been heard of him for a month except a rumour that he had gone to Florence.

"Severn, I am most terribly distressed. I had no idea poor Keats had gone," he said, pacing up and down the studio. "You see, I went in such a hurry. I had intended writing but I never had a minute. She completely monopolised my time. She wouldn't let me——"

"She?" queried Severn.

"That vampire, that nymphomaniac, that gorgon! Severn, I tell you, she is the most impossible, insatiable egotist that ever lived!" he cried excitedly, his cheeks flushed.

"I am still in the dark. The last time I saw you, you were going to dine with Princess Borghese," said Severn.

"I dined with her. I was there again the next day. She told me that on the morrow she was going to her villa near Lucca. She invited me to go with her. It was a travelling circus, my dear Severn. Twenty-two of us—her chamberlain, her ladies-in-waiting, two grooms of the chamber, two pages, an enormous negro whom she had married off to her French maid because people said it was indecent for him to carry her from her bath to her boudoir, her secretary, her masseuse, her doctor, an Italian composer she has turned into a lap-dog, and a troop of cooks, serving-maids, pony-boys and a tame priest!"

"How long did you stay? You left here in February."

"My dear fellow, in some moods the Princess was the most enchanting woman, and then you forgot what a devil she could be. After a week at Lucca she decided to go to Venice to hear her composer's new opera. He conducted, Colibran singing. The place went mad over them. Then we all moved off to Trieste for another performance. She has a sister living there, Murat's widow— you remember they shot him five years ago—she's in exile there with her two boys. All the time I wanted to get back here, but she wouldn't hear of it; and then on to Bologna we went, still following the maestro. In Bologna one night he smacked her face. There was a scene that was sheer grand opera. She fainted, the ladies-in-waiting screamed, the chamberlain brandished a pistol and bellowed. Her Nino burst into tears——"

"Nino?" asked Severn.

"Nino Pacini, the Sicilian composer. Do you remember that day when we were on the Pincio and she drove by, and poor Keats rushed off? He was with her in the carriage. She adores him and tantalises him to death. I quite expected that he would stick a knife in me and I should be carried off, like some scene in a Sicilian drama. But not at all! I took some of the strain off him. After the slapping affair, she took to her bed for four days and held court there. She received the Abbess of a convent for orphan girls, had twenty of them presented to her, gave them each a present and made them a most beautiful speech on the moral virtues! The next morning she breakfasted in bed with Nino who was forgiven everything. The Cardinal-Archbishop came to lunch and Pacini sang some notes from Palestrina so divinely that the Cardinal, a dear old man, wept and gave Nino a special blessing. The next day we left for Lucca again. Nino went to Vienna, but the Princess couldn't go, as it's forbidden ground to all the Bonapartes. At Milan I fell ill and couldn't go on. I was utterly exhausted, and disgusted with myself. I had started off feeling a figure of romance. I ended feeling like a cheap *cicisbèo*."

"A *cicisbèo*?" queried Severn.

"That's a good old Italian tradition. Tired husbands hire young gallants to attend their wives. It gives each party variety. I don't know why I tell you all this, Severn. It probably disgusts you. Well, it disgusts me, and a sick dog's returned to its kennel."

Elton lay back in the chair, as elegant as ever, but he had an air of fatigue. His thin, handsome features seemed sharper, his fine, well-bred hands more transparent.

"You said you were ill in Milan. Are you better?" asked Severn.

Elton made no answer for a few moments.

"I have often thought of that scene on the Pincio when poor Keats rushed off. You explained to me the cause. The flirtatious Princess recalled a girl he loved in London, a girl he could never marry in his condition. Poor devil! But you didn't know, my dear Severn, that you were explaining all this to another poor devil in exactly the same situation! Two years ago I fell in love with one of the sweetest girls in England. My parents approved of her. I returned to my regiment engaged. When I came home again we were to be married. We were stationed at Gibraltar. We had a pack of hounds that the Duke of Wellington kept on his estate in Spain, and we hunted two days a week. One day we were caught in a rainstorm. It was in April, with a wind like a knife coming off the Sierras. When I got back that night I had a fever. In the middle of the night I had a frightful coughing bout and brought up blood. I have been coughing blood ever since—not badly, only occasionally. They sent me home. The doctors thought I couldn't survive a winter in England, so I was shipped out here, like poor Keats. Now you know how I felt when he bolted that day. I am an exile, damned. I may never see my fiancée again. I can never marry."

"Isn't that losing hope too soon? Many recover, if care is taken," said Severn. "You are full of energy; you look very well."

Elton bent down and adjusted the strap of his trousers. Then he looked up, all the misery of his soul speaking through his eyes.

"I look very well, Severn. I am so well that I am driven mad with desire for any pretty woman who gives me a look. They say it is a pathological passion, the thrust of the dying species to reproduce itself. Nature has given me a set-up that makes it easy. You artist fellows are always borrowing my head. Gibson the sculptor asked me to pose for Adonis, with an arrow in his thigh." He jumped up and crossed the room to the fireplace, where he stood, head down, gripping the mantelpiece. "Severn, he should have given me an arrow in the lung!"

He swung round violently and thumped his chest with a clenched fist while the tears stood in his eyes. "It is here I am slain, Severn, here! I have so little time. I clutch **at**

E

every pleasure—I disgrace myself—but Severn, Severn, I have so little time! I am so young!"

Severn went to him, gripped him by the arms and looked quietly at the agonised face before him.

"Because you are so young, there is time, there is hope," he said quietly. "Will you tell me what happened in Milan? How ill were you?"

"It's the usual story—a temperature, coughing, a hæmorrhage," replied Elton. "I didn't come here to tell you this. When I heard of Keats's death I was distressed, but I was not surprised. It was so obvious. Severn, I must tell you the truth. I am a coward. I battled with myself to come and see you, but every time I looked at that poor fellow I saw my own future. I ran away, to forget, to get away from myself. I leapt at the invitation to Lucca. I felt I must get out of Rome before his end came. Forgive me, Severn."

"There is nothing to forgive," replied Severn, putting an arm around him. "But you must not let your imagination torture you. You must have faith."

"You are kind and understanding. I shouldn't tell you all this—you who have gone through so much. All Rome talks of you."

"Of me? But why? It's ridiculous!" protested Severn.

"I hear everyone speak of you. All the English here know the story of your devotion to Keats."

Embarrassed, Severn made no response. He looked at his watch. It was noon.

"I eat at a little *trattoria* round the corner. I've some friends there, German artists who live at the end of the street. They are gay company. Won't you join us?" he asked, taking off his painting smock.

Elton's face lit up, the sunshine of youth in it again.

"Of course I will! I should like that. It is always nice to be with you," he replied.

II

It was quite true what Elton had said. The story of a young English poet's death had gone around Rome. The English colony became curious to see the young man who had nursed him so devotedly. It became a romantic story of unknown genius dying in poverty which they would have been so glad to alleviate had they but known. The English abroad should stand by one another, even when those in need did not belong to one's class. Mr Severn, it seemed, was an artist, struggling. Perhaps they could buy some of his work to help him.

The English aristocracy wintering in Rome spent much of its time buying things. They frequented the studios of the painters and sculptors, provided they were famous. It made a morning excursion every bit as delightful as going to the great piazza in front of St Peter's to see the Pope come out to give his annual blessing to the donkeys of Rome, or riding out along the Via Appia past all the ruined sepulchres of ancient Rome families, or seeing a sarcophagus or a bust that had been disinterred from the sleep of centuries. It was an era that craved new sensations, new fashions, new themes for gossip. A moderate taste for literature and art was condoned. The boys at Eton were flogged into construing Latin authors, the easy ones without a crib, the difficult authors with one. There was some fluency in Greek and Latin, but any attempt to read English was discouraged. Only "saps" indulged such odd tastes. Byron, of course, everyone read. He was a peer as well as a poet, and the scandal of his private life, first in England and now in Italy, had made him an international character. Mr Wordsworth was preferred by the intelligentsia, who professed enthusiasm for a long, tedious poem called *The Excursion*, which, oddly enough, had no movement in it.

The fevers of the French Revolution and the upheavals

of the Napoleonic era had shaken the fabric of polite society. The august ladies of a despotic conclave that presided over the membership of Almack's, particularly Lady Jersey and the Princess Lieven, had succeeded in banning from its precincts the Duke of Wellington, whose notorious liaison with Mrs Arbuthnot was too serious to overlook even in the nation's hero. They firmly denounced that indelicate article of masculine attire, tight-fitting pantaloons. But that licentious new dance, the waltz, imported from Germany, became such a craze that they had to recognise it. Mr Theodore Hook attacked General Thornton of the Guards so violently for having praised a dance calculated to lead to the most licentious circumstances that the General challenged Mr Hook to a duel, on account of which he was compelled to resign his commission. But the Emperor Alexander of Russia put his seal on the waltz by dancing it twice at Almack's, after which a proposal to present a petition to Parliament against it as a national danger was dropped. Byron had his cynical doubts concerning such zestful promiscuity of the sexes:

> *The breast thus publicly resigned to man*
> *In private may resist him—if it can.*

It was the era of rival salons, that of Lady Holland's and of the Countess of Jersey's. They were both powerful tyrants, but Lady Holland's field was restricted. The eldest son of the house had been born out of wedlock. Happily, he was in love with Miss Mary FitzClarence, daughter of the Duke of Clarence, also born out of wedlock, and there seemed to be no social impediment to that match. The King had done well by his brother's three bastards. The boy was made Earl of Munster, the two girls had the rank of an earl's daughters. It was also the era of Continental travel. The nightmare of Napoleon had passed. The English, never so happy as when they can leave the island they love so dearly and draw attention to the inferiority of life and character everywhere abroad, began to cross the Channel and appear on the great highways that ran through France, Switzerland, Italy and Germany. Two centres above all others held their affection, Paris and Rome. The winter climate of the latter drew them south. Over the St Bernard Pass they came clattering in great coaches that finally rested row upon row in the Piazza di Spagna. Their owners moved into vast palaces where they took suites for the season, to the benefit of the proud, impoverished Roman aristocracy, who with Titians and Raphaels on the walls could scarcely afford fires in their grates.

No city offered a greater variety of entertainment to its visitors. There was the endless pageantry that surrounded the Pope and his Cardinals, semi-divine, semiregal in their ambience. There was no life in the city free of the dominance of the Church, which owned everything, controlled everything. All its offices of government were occupied by ecclesiastics. It could promote, reward, imprison or banish the inhabitants of the city-state with the unchallengeable power of a despot. One hundred years behind the rest of Europe, Russia excluded, it presented all the attractions of a medieval state in colour and ceremony, in a setting that enshrined the memorials of two thousand years. The English who dwelt in Rome through the winter months were mostly drawn from the aristocracy, which had the means to transport itself across the English Channel and over the Alps accompanied by an army of grooms, valets and maids. To the social attractions of balls and soirées in the great palaces and hunting on the Campagna were added such diversions as the collection of antiquities and the patronage of art for those who aspired to intellectual pursuits. Lastly there was the world of fashion. To the horde of Roman princes and princesses, dukes and duchesses, marquises and marchionesses, counts and countesses, barons and baronesses, with pedigrees real and faked that reached back to the Rome of the Cæsars, were added the resounding names of Britain's great families. In the winter of 1820-1 Rome housed, in the magnificent settings of its palaces and villas, the Duchess of Devonshire, perhaps the leader, although somewhat of a blue-stocking with her passion for excavating, the Duke of Bedford, his brother Lord William Russell, the Duke of Hamilton, Lord and Lady Ruthven, Lord Colchester, Lady Compton and that tireless, witty, beautiful and exasperating woman, the Countess of Westmorland. Around these luminaries of wealth and rank congregated a cluster of baronets, knights and landed gentry with wives and daughters who moved across the Roman scene with regal elegance. From October to May they diverted themselves by day and night until the approach of the summer heat sent them lumbering northwards again in their great coaches.

There was another English colony, much smaller, more serious and yet gayer despite its impoverished state. This consisted of the artists, very young men mostly who worked in the galleries and studios, leading lives of ecstatic endeavour and immeasurable ambition. They had no coaches standing in the Piazza di Spagna, no servants, no horses, no drafts on the Bank of Torlonia. They lived in holes and corners, plentiful enough in a warren where fragments of the palaces of the Cæsars were converted into honeycombs for the shelters of the poor. They were artists treading the cobbled alleys and worn stairs of their great predecessors, Raphael, Michelangelo, Cellini, Titian, Perugino, Botticelli, Pinturicchio, and Bernini. In a brotherhood composed of art, youth and happy poverty they possessed a Rome unknown to their fellow country-men who were put to bed by valets and maids, who never sat at the bare crowded tables of a *trattoria*. On bread, spaghetti and cheap wine these young men nurtured dreams of immortality.

To this brotherhood of artists, drawn from all races and classes, some in easy, some in desperate circumstances, Severn found himself freely admitted. But by chance he was carried into other circles in a manner and with a speed that left him dazed. In that sad dawn at the graveside of his friend scarcely two months ago he had been introduced by Ewing to an unknown young man, Seymour Kirkup, a fellow art student who had come out of sympathy to pay respect to a fellow exile. He was a young man in the early thirties, of medium height with a fair English complexion. The first thing strangers observed was the charm of his manner combined with a beautiful speaking voice. He dressed well, and his agreeable personality and quick intelligence made him a welcome guest in the palaces of Rome. His acquaintances were not confined to the English colony. Fluent in French and Italian, he was considered *simpatico* by the Italians. The son of a London diamond merchant, he had comfortable means and was of a kindly disposition. Severn ever recalled with gratitude his conduct during those days following Keats's death when he had taken him to his apartment insisting that he should remain there until he was rested. It was only after a few weeks, when their acquaintanceship ripened into a warm regard of each other, that Severn learned something of his history. He, too, was an Academy Gold Medallist. Then, four years ago, detecting a pulmonary weakness, the doctor advised him to reside in a less rigorous climate, and he had come to Rome. "No hardship, for I love being here. I am well, happy and as industrious as my mood warrants," he said to Severn, describing his life in Rome. "Perhaps I am too social, but young Englishmen are at a premium here, with most of them up in the sixties, so why not make the best of it?"

He certainly did make the best of it. He kept a hunter for riding in the Campagna, a gig for riding in the park. His establishment consisted of an Italian cook-housekeeper and a husband who appeared in the various rôles of groom, valet, waiter and occasionally model, for he had the body of an Apollo. He presented a problem. He was under constant threat of dismissal for beating his wife, but the dismissal of Mario involved the dismissal of Nina. "Imagine my relief one day," said Kirkup to Severn, "when after warning Nina that they would have to go if these scenes went on, she said 'Signore, it is nothing. Mario beats me because he's jealous. If he wasn't jealous I should know he had another woman. *Che vuole?*' "

It was Kirkup who began to take Severn to houses he would never have penetrated. He had become something of a legend unwillingly. The story of the tragic death of the young English poet, of the devoted friend who had nursed him in his fatal illness, a poor young artist who had journeyed out from England with his dying friend, circulated through the English Colony. When Kirkup told them he had been at the young poet's funeral and had housed his artist friend in his rooms, they asked to be taken to see him. Kirkup, hoping some commissions might arise, brought his aristocratic friends to the little studio where Severn was labouring on his Academy picture from sunrise to sundown. They were still more interested when they discovered that Mr Severn was a young man of an extremely handsome appearance, with easy manners and a charming personality.

One morning, about eleven o'clock, a carriage with a coachman and attendant groom in livery drew up before the entrance to the studio in the Via San Isidoro. It created something of a sensation with its splendid pair of horses, its trappings and its occupants. Out of it stepped

Seymour Kirkup and a lady of the most striking beauty, dressed with arresting elegance. She was a woman in the late thirties, but any sense of age was dismissed by the vivacity of her expression and manner. Witty as well as beautiful, a linguist, a musician, with a devastating zest for life, she was considered to be the most vivacious member of the aristocratic colony living in Rome. The Duchess of Devonshire may have exceeded her in rank, but Nature had endowed her with such a vital personality that she became the natural centre of any circle she frequented. There were many who were afraid of her. She could be arrogant and domineering. Her wit sometimes struck like a stiletto. Rich, extravagant, her sense of *décor* was flawless, whether in the presentation of herself or the furnishing of her establishment. There was little cordiality between her and the Duchess of Devonshire. The latter, unostentatious, serious-minded, and regarded as a "blue stocking," looked upon her rival as a frivolous and unpredictable woman, vain, assertive and, her background considered, ill-bred.

Severn was at his easel when he heard a knock on the door of his small studio. Opening the door, he found Kirkup and a resplendent lady wearing an enormous pleated silk bonnet and a blue cashmere shawl over a plum-coloured velvet costume.

"I have brought the Countess of Westmorland to see you," said Kirkup, and, turning to the lady, "Let me present Mr Joseph Severn," he added.

She advanced into the room like a queen, gave Severn a dazzling smile and accepted the chair he proffered. She glanced round the room, noticing its sparse, shabby furniture. But the young man was something to look at. He had the most beautiful eyes, with well-defined eyebrows. Above a fine brow a mass of chestnut curls crowned his well-shaped head. His hair was a little long over the nape of his neck, and his white stock was frayed and badly tied, but it was a head of classic beauty. The nose was straight with sensitive nostrils, the mouth with its cupid's bow was a shade feminine, but redeemed by the strong chin. Why had Kirkup not prepared her for meeting this very handsome young man? His figure was good, his hands refined, his complexion healthy. A quick intelligence shone in his eyes.

She noted all these things rapidly as she took the chair he offered gracefully. Even the paint-daubed smock he wore became him, emphasising his youth with its suggestion of babyhood. Surely this was the poet, not the artist, of the sad story that had gone round Rome?

"Mr Kirkup is very kind to bring me—I fear we are interrupting your work. May I ask what it is you are painting—the subject?" she said, in a voice full of charm and amiability.

"It's my picture for the Royal Academy competition. I fear it is in a very rough state. Your ladyship is probably aware of the story of Alcibiades. He was——"

She interrupted him with a little laugh, smiling up at him.

"Mr Severn, I warn you I am a very ignorant woman in anything concerning history. That he was a Greek I know, but that is all. Pray explain the picture to me," she said.

"With pleasure, your ladyship," he replied, a little overwhelmed. Should he say "My lady," "Your ladyship" or "Countess"? Two days ago Kirkup had brought the Duke and Duchess of Bedford to his studio. That was simple. You said "Your Grace" to either of them.

He paused and her eyes rested on him with such gentleness that he blushed.

"Alcibiades, as your ladyship may know, at the end of his life was in exile on his way to the court of Artaxerxes.

One night a mob of armed men went to his house. He rushed out on them, sword in hand, to defend himself, and fell pierced with a shower of arrows. I have chosen this moment when he comes out of his house—the mob below, the house burning behind, his figure silhouetted against the flames. I fear as it is at present the conception is rather confused," he concluded apologetically.

"But how very interesting, Mr. Severn! I hope that I shall be permitted to see it before it goes to London?" she asked. "Mr Kirkup must warn me when it is completed."

"It is most kind of you, Lady Westmorland. I shall feel honoured."

Her eyes fell on a miniature standing on a small table. She picked it up.

"Who are these, Mr Severn? What a charming group!" she exclaimed.

"That's my mother and father, and my three sisters and two brothers. I painted it just before I left England."

"What a delightful family. You must feel homesick?"

"I am, my lady, but I try and forget it in my work. We are very attached to one another."

"And what is your father, Mr Severn?" asked Lady Westmorland. The extremely well-bred air of this attractive young man made her wonder what kind of a background he had sprung from.

"My father teaches music, but he has a passion for art," replied Severn.

"Ah, then it is in the blood. Artists are born, not made," she commented.

"But there's a lot of self-making has to be done also. We work very hard," exclaimed Kirkup.

She laughed gaily at his observation, and addressed Severn.

"Mr Kirkup, as perhaps you know, is one of the gayest young men in Rome, and the most popular. I am glad to say he never seems to allow work to prevent him from giving us his delightful company," said Lady Westmorland, replacing the miniature on the table. "I am sure there must be a great demand for exquisite miniatures like this."

"I hope there will be, but at present I have no customers except Lord Ruthven, who has commissioned a miniature of his daughter," said Severn.

"Then we must see to it that you have clients. Seymour, we must make Mr Severn the fashion," said Lady Westmorland, rising.

"I'm sure you could bring that about," replied Kirkup, happy to see his plan succeeding.

"We must not interrupt you any longer, Mr Severn. Forgive us this sudden intrusion. Could you lunch with me to-morrow at my villa—a small party. Seymour, bring Mr Severn along."

She did not wait for Severn's acceptance. He was aware that it was a command. In any case, he would have let nothing interfere with this exciting invitation.

"Then *arrivederci* until to-morrow, Mr Severn."

She extended a delicate gloved hand over which Severn bowed, smiled at him with her beautiful eyes, and left the studio.

Severn followed them down the stairs to the splendid equipage waiting in the street. He bowed low as it went off with a proud clatter of hooves, coachman and groom in yellow and buff liveries on the box, a coronet on the panel of the open landau.

Severn went back to his studio. The bedroom door was open. Thank heavens he had made his bed. Then suddenly he blushed with confusion. He had forgotten all about the shirt he had washed out. It was hanging with a pair of white stockings on a line at the end of the room, behind the easel. It must have been in full view of Lady

Westmorland during her visit. How sympathetic she was, and what a lovely woman, and how exquisitely dressed!

He recalled the first occasion on which he had seen her, not knowing who she was. He had gone one day, soon after his arrival in Rome, to call on John Gibson, an English sculptor, the favourite pupil of Canova. Despite the fact that he was only thirty years of age, Gibson had a considerable reputation. The son of a working gardener from Wales, as a youth he had dreamed of being carried by an eagle to Rome, where he would find fame. At twenty-five he had exhibited at the Royal Academy, and a year later was in Rome, where Canova received him most graciously. "I am rich. I am anxious to be of use to you as long as you stay in Rome," said the famous old sculptor. Two years later the young Duke of Devonshire bought his *Mars and Cupid* for his collection at Chatsworth, and last year Sir George Beaumont, a connoisseur, had bought his *Psyche and the Zephyrs*. Severn called to see him, very diffidently, for what young man so prosperous would want to bother with an unknown artist? But Gibson had been most cordial. He had not been very long in the studio before there was another visitor, an elderly man. The studio in the Via Fontanella was very large. Half a dozen statues unfinished or completed revealed Gibson's industry. The walls were hung with casts. The visitor was anxious to see the *Mars and Cupid* bought by the Duke of Devonshire. Gibson undraped it. He also showed them his first work in Rome, a sleeping shepherd boy which had been greatly admired. The elderly visitor was perhaps a prospective customer, so Severn kept in the background as much as possible. Then, hearing Gibson address his visitor as "My Lord," he felt shyer than before. At last, with many compliments to the sculptor, his lordship departed.

"Now we can talk!" said Gibson, smiling and ploughing his hand through his thick black hair. "That was Lord

Colchester, a friend of the Duchess of Devonshire. Thorwaldsen warned me that he looks and looks, but never buys—but I make a rule of never suggesting that they should buy. Perhaps one can't afford to buy on only four thousand a year!" said Gibson with a chuckle.

"Four thousand a year—but that's a fortune!" cried Severn.

"Not as fortunes go with many of the English here. They spend more than that in a season buying pictures. Lord Colchester had a good head, don't you think? I would like to do a bust. I think a head that's counted so many heads should be saved for posterity!" said Gibson. Then, seeing a look of perplexity on Severn's face, he added: "Ah, you didn't know Lord Colchester created the first Census and had all our heads counted? He was the Speaker of the House of Commons and is now living here on his pension."

The young sculptor took off the white smock he was wearing, opened a cupboard and brought out two glasses and a bottle of wine.

"Now tell me," he said, handing Severn a glass. "What are you studying particularly? Can I help in any way?"

Severn told him of his hope of gaining the Royal Academy Travelling Scholarship. After a pleasant talk, he rose to go, overwhelmed by the kindness of his young host. Gibson escorted him to the door. A carriage had drawn up and a lady was descending from it. He observed a swift look of annoyance on Gibson's face and heard him exclaim involuntarily, "*Dio mio!*" Then he went forward to greet her politely.

Severn recalled this visit to Gibson's studio. His visitor this morning was the lady whom he had seen calling on Gibson. Why had his amiable host seemed perturbed by the visit of a lady so charming and influential as the Countess of Westmorland? Was it because, like Lord

Colchester, she was another of those who came and looked and never bought? Had she promised to help Gibson also in finding clients? Perhaps it would be foolish to place any reliance on promises so lightly made. His father had had many bitter experiences of the whims of the rich.

Nevertheless, he felt greatly exhilarated by her visit. One thing became clear. If he was to make any progress with people like Lady Westmorland, Lord Ruthven, and other members of the aristocracy, he could not continue to live in a tiny studio, or to do his washing in it. Yet at present he dared not strain his very slender resources. If he won the Academy pension, how different his lot would be.

III

The Countess of Westmorland drove back to the Villa Negroni having dropped Seymour Kirkup at his studio. She had enjoyed her excursion. She liked to think of herself as a patroness of the arts. She had no intention of allowing the Duchess of Devonshire to enjoy a monopoly of that rôle. Mr Joseph Severn had been a very pleasant surprise. On the whole she did not find artists very much to her taste. They were often ill-kempt, ill-mannered and very bourgeois. She exempted the Marquis Canova and Herr Thorwaldsen from such criticisms. Even had they been socially objectionable, they were artists of international fame, which excused everything, since genius could not be judged by ordinary standards of conduct. There was nothing against Mr Severn's appearance— indeed, there was very much in favour of it. He was exceptionally handsome, his manners were good, and he was, in Rome to-day, a figure of interest by virtue of the story of his devotion to that dead poet, of whom no one seemed to have heard.

By the time her carriage, mounting the hill, had reached the crossways by the Fontana dell'Acqua Felice,

whose spouting lions made a pleasant sound in the warm
April noonday, she had decided to advance the career of
young Mr Severn.

At the very moment when Lady Westmorland entered
her villa resolved on taking Mr Severn in hand, the same
young gentleman received a letter whose contents raised
him into the seventh heaven of happiness. It was from
Lord Ruthven expressing his pleasure with the miniature
of his daughter. He enclosed a draft on Child's Bank,
London, for the sum of fifteen guineas. It arrived at a
crisis in the affairs of the artist and gave him two whole
months in which he could work on his Academy picture.
It was a singular interweaving of Fate that on the morning of Lady Westmorland's visit he should have received
a draft on Child's Bank. The lady of fashion and the
impecunious student were thus brought into a relationship
of which neither was aware.

In the year 1656 a goldsmith of London signed an in-
denture for eight years with a fourteen-year-old lad from
Wiltshire. After a few years the apprentice met and fell
in love with a nineteen-year-old girl, Elizabeth Wheeler.
Mrs Wheeler, her widowed mother, had married a man
named Blanchard employed by her former husband, who
had left behind him a flourishing goldsmith's business at
the sign of the Marigold, next door to Temple Bar. Into
this business Blanchard took as partner in 1671 the young
employee Francis Child who had married his step-
daughter. The name Wheeler fell out and the two partners
conducted the business under the name Blanchard and
Child. This firm was among the goldsmiths "that kept
running cashes."

The Sign of the Marigold was printed on the drafts
issued by Blanchard and Child, and thus it was that, one
hundred and fifty years later, young Severn wondered at
this device as he hurried to the Banca Torlonia with Lord

Ruthven's draft drawn on Child's Bank of Temple Bar, London.

When Blanchard died, Francis Child inherited the business. He dropped the goldsmith's part and became simply a banker, and as such the father of the profession. By then, at the age of forty, he found himself a well-to-do man with a prosperous business which had had the most distinguished customers, having transacted the financial affairs of Oliver Cromwell, Nell Gwynn, Barbara Villiers, the notorious Duchess of Cleveland, mistress of Charles II, and in contrast with the rewards of harlotry the affairs also of Archbishop Tenison, Prince Rupert, Pepys and Dryden.

In the same year that Francis Child inherited the business he entered politics. He was a man of good standing in official circles, and when a lottery was held for the late Prince Rupert's jewels, Child was entrusted with its conduct, a matter in which Charles II took so much interest that he himself counted the lottery tickets at Whitehall. Now a figure in the Corporation and a man of considerable wealth, William III knighted him at a Lord Mayor's Banquet in 1689. Nine years later he was elected Lord Mayor, and provided such a pageant in the Lord Mayor's Procession as had never been seen before. He was wealthy enough to lend the overspent Government large sums of money.

The time had come for him to move from his modest home at Fulham. He bought the former family seat of Sir Thomas Gresham, Osterley Park, built with a fortune made as agent of Henry VIII in the Low Countries. Sir Francis had three sons and three daughters. The two elder sons died without heirs, and Osterley Park passed to Samuel, the youngest son. His son Francis, succeeding to the property in 1761, set about to transform the great mansion from a Tudor into a Palladian palace. He called

F

in Robert Adam. It was a masterpiece of conversion. It was not completed when Francis Child died young, on the eve of marriage. His brother Robert succeeded. He continued to embellish the great mansion. He had no son and heir. All his wealth and Osterley Park devolved upon an only daughter. He cherished her as a precious possession. Failing to achieve the perpetuation of his name, he had it firmly in his mind that any suitor for his daughter's hand must adopt the name of Child. In view of the fact that Sarah Child was one of the great heiresses of the age, and young and beautiful withal, marriage into one of the great titled families was easily within her reach. Dukes, marquises and earls gravitated towards such a wonderful bait. Dutiful to her father's fiat, she rejected in turn Lord Blandford, the son of the Duke of Marlborough, and the Marquis of Graham, both highly eligible in every respect except that they could not take the name of Child or produce for him a grandchild of that name who would carry on the famous bank.

But love is stronger than a father's wishes and conquers the heart of the most dutiful of daughters. Sarah at the age of twenty proceeded to do exactly what Mr Child had determined she should not do. She fell wildly in love with a dashing young officer of twenty-two. Unhappily, this young man had the same disqualification as a suitor in the eyes of Mr Child. He was John Fane, the tenth Earl of Westmorland. Despite the tearful appeal of his beloved daughter, he firmly forbade the marriage. The young nobleman would not let himself be frustrated by an obstinate and unreasonable father. One evening while dining with Mr Child he asked him, "If you were in love with a girl whose father refused his consent to the union, what would you do?"

"Why, run away with her to be sure," replied Mr Child. Early one morning in May, 1782, a closed phaeton with a pair of swift horses and a postillion outrider waited in the shade of a grove outside the high wall by Osterley Park. By it paced a young man. He had not long to wait before Sarah Child came towards him, having slipped out of one of the side gates. A swift embrace and they were in the phaeton, which set off at a hot pace across the country, making for the great North Road that led them to Gretna Green. Unfortunately, a lodge-keeper had seen the young lady's flight and had carried the news to the great house, where Mr Child, at breakfast, quickly guessed the purpose and destination of the run-away pair. He lost no time in sending off two servants in pursuit. They came up with the runaways at Baldock, but a servant of Lord Westmorland's shot the horse of one of the pursuers to prevent him from getting ahead and detaining the relay horses at the next stage. The pursuers turned tail. Lord Westmorland and his bride reached Gretna Green and were united by the "priest," a toll-keeper in his toll-house, which functioned as a church. For a fee of a guinea, the runaways became man and wife.

Mr Child, faced with a situation he could not change, recognised the marriage. He consented to a church ceremony, but stayed away. His resentment was revealed in his will when he died. He passed over his daughter and the firstborn male of the marriage who would inherit the title, and left his fortune to the second son and, failing him, to the eldest daughter. Since only one son, Lord Burghersh, the future eleventh Earl of Westmorland, was born of the marriage, the Child fortune passed to his sister, Lady Sarah Sophia Child Fane, then six years old. Lord Westmorland's wife, after bearing him a disinherited heir and five daughters, died at the age of thirty-one while in Ireland with her husband, then holding the post of Lord Lieutenant of Ireland.

Seven years later Lord Westmorland married again.

He chose another heiress, Miss Jane Saunders, who gave him four sons and two daughters. The second Countess, rich, beautiful, witty, was not the kind of woman to play the rôle of a meek wife. Her husband, now Lord Privy Seal, protested in vain against her ebullient conduct in society, her tireless activities, her routs, balls and entertainments, to which she invited all the world. The romantic young man who had run away to get married now wished he could run away from his second wife. Their quarrels became the talk of the town. The mother of six growing children, she seemed outrageously frivolous to many. There were others who found the Earl overbearing and odious. "He is coarse in mind, manners and language. I do not wonder he is accused of having sowed the seeds of rebellion in Ireland," wrote Lady Holland to a friend. After nine years of married life and growing dissension, the Earl and his wife separated. She left him the care of the six children, vowing she would never sleep under his roof again. In turn he tried for some time to collect evidence that would enable him to have her committed as a person of irresponsible conduct. "But really in order to avoid the expense of a separate maintenance," observed Lady Holland with all the detestation of a Whig for a hated Tory.

Lady Westmorland set up a separate establishment in London. She soon found that she could not compete with the brilliant salon of Lady Holland or with her gifted and beautiful step-daughter, Lady Sarah Sophia Fane, who, having married the fifth Earl of Jersey, was established at Osterley Park, heiress of the great house, the fortune and the bank of her grandfather. She, in turn, had defeated his wish, for in marrying a peer she produced a titled son. The name of Child died out.

The abdication of Napoleon and his internment on the Isle of Elba, with the return of the Bourbons to Paris, resulted in a flood of English tourists crossing the Channel to enjoy the extraordinary sight of the Cossacks camping in the Bois de Boulogne, and Wellington, Blücher, King Frederick William IV, the Czar Alexander, Talleyrand and Metternich attending the soirées of the restored Bourbon aristocracy. The Congress of Vienna beckoned Lady Westmorland next as a spectacle not to be missed. For six months she kept open house for the representatives of five nations, until the bombshell of Napoleon's escape from Elba resulted in a general flight homewards. By the end of 1816, the bogey of Napoleon having been permanently disposed of, Lady Westmorland returned to the Continent. To winter in Rome had become the fashion, following the trail blazed by the widowed Duchess of Devonshire. Lady Westmorland, her baggage contained in four coaches, and with a train of five servants, arrived in Rome, to which she brought the gaiety of her person and an income that enabled her to live in considerable state in the Villa Negroni, of which she leased the *piano nobile* and lower floor. It had a range of superb salons that overlooked a garden with terraces, orangeries, pergolas and fountains in which, so the legend ran, forty years earlier, Alfieri had meditated and composed his tragedy *Antigone* while living in the adjacent Villa Strozzi, from which he conducted his liaison with the truant wife of Bonnie Prince Charlie under the very nose of her guileless guardian, Henry, Cardinal Duke of York.

For four seasons now Lady Westmorland had held court in her villa. The *beau monde* flocked there in preference to the more sedate salon of the Duchess of Devonshire, where no gambling was permitted. An accomplished linguist, speaking French, Italian, German and Spanish, well read, an excellent pianist, and gifted with a good voice, these assets were enhanced by Lady Westmorland's natural talent and zest for entertainment, her brilliance as a conversationalist. Vain, erratic, extravagant, agitated by violent enthusiasms or irrational hatred, she had the command of an invincible charm. At forty-one she was still a young woman with enormous zest for life. By nature she was a crusader.

Now for the moment she had a task in hand. That remarkable young man in a miserable room with his shirt hung on a line must be helped.

CHAPTER V

I

A FOOTMAN in a green and gold livery showed Kirkup and Severn on to the terrace of the Villa Negroni. They were the first to arrive for the luncheon party. They passed through a vast entrance hall with frescoed walls in which rose a wide marble staircase. From the coolness of this great hall they went out into the warm sunshine of the April day. Severn gave a cry of astonishment when he saw the garden with its terraces and fountains. The villa was the property of Prince Massimo, who lived in his palace down towards the Tiber. It was a summer villa set among gardens and had the appearance of a country estate far away from any city, although it was only half an hour's walk from Kirkup's apartment. It had long been considered among the most beautiful villas in Rome. It was renowned for its magnificent avenues of cypresses, and its long, wide terraces lined with orange trees and spaced with ancient sarcophagi and old Roman terra-cotta wine jars. At the end of the avenue of cypresses, a fountain threw a jet of water thirty feet high. In an alcove stood a massive statue of Minerva from a Roman temple. It had been placed there by a former occupant of the villa, Cardinal Montalto, later Pope Sixtus V, who, born the son of a swineherd, had risen to the Pontiff's throne.

As was so frequently the case in Rome, this glorious villa had a tragic history. Here had lived the beautiful Vittoria Accoramboni, married to Francesco Peretti, a nephew of the Cardinal. She was adored by her husband, by his mother Camilla, and by her uncle-in-law the Cardinal. The rich and powerful old Prince Orsini lusted after her, smitten by her beauty. He contrived a means of disposing of her handsome husband. A bargain was made with Vittoria's brothers, who decoyed Peretti and murdered him. On the day, April 24, 1585, that her uncle Cardinal Montalto was installed as Pope Sixtus V, Vittoria was married to the lecherous old Prince. The bargain with the brothers had been completed. Six months later her husband died, leaving her a great fortune in jewels. The dispossessed members of the Orsini family sent a gang of forty masked assassins to her country house. They seized the young Princess Orsini. One assassin as he pressed home his dagger under her left breast demanded, probing, whether it had reached her heart. They next massacred her brother and then went off with the strong box containing the jewels.

Nothing of that tragedy haunted the villa to-day. The glory and peace of a Roman spring lay over the gardens. Under a long pergola of mauve wistaria whose heavy clusters filled the air with perfume, a table had been set for twenty. Near this pergola was a Judas tree laden with heliotrope blossom. The urns surmounting the long stone balustrade held cascades of crimson geraniums. Masses of roses covered the terrace walls. It was a sight to intoxicate the senses.

Severn and his friend, at the sound of voices, turned from contemplation of this paradise. Lady Westmorland, accompanied by some of her guests, came along the terrace. She greeted Severn and Kirkup with much animation, and then presented them. Severn, preoccupied and dazed by the beauty of the setting, did not hear the names of his fellow guests. They were all dressed in the height of fashion, the ladies adding much gaiety to the scene with their bonnets and silk dresses. Lady Westmorland was almost flamboyant in a pleated gown of green silk with *broderie anglaise*. She wore a wide-brimmed Leghorn hat. A rope of pearls adorned her beautiful neck. Her musical laughter and gracious manner dominated the distinguished company. The last to arrive was a Cardinal in his purple-edged robes.

They took their places at the table according to their name cards. Half a dozen Italian footmen under a major-domo began to serve them. Severn's quick eye noted the splendid Capodimonte table vases laden with roses and the green-and-gold Sèvres china service with the Orsini crest.

Presently he was engaged in conversation by the lady on his right. She was an elderly woman, possibly in the sixties, with clear, intelligent eyes that gazed at Severn in a manner suggesting that of all this company he interested her most. She had a soft speaking voice, and though age had taken her beauty there was great distinction in her features. She was heavily powdered and grey hair peeped out from under her enormous hat. She wore a thin collar of emeralds. Beautiful rings glittered on her long thin fingers. She suggested a portrait by Reynolds or Gainsborough.

"You must tell me your name, young man. I never hear names when I'm introduced. Are you new to Rome?" she asked.

"Yes," responded Severn quietly. "My name is Severn. I have been here about five months."

She saw that he was shy and noticed his extremely sensitive face. He had a good brow, and a fine head of dark curls.

"Are you a musician or an artist—or travelling just for pleasure?" she asked, smiling at him.

"An artist, I hope, ma'am."

"Ah, then my guess was good. Of course, it is always foolish to think artists look like artists or poets look like poets—though I knew two of them who did. Indeed, I

should say one who did and one who does. For Alfieri is
dead and Lord Byron is alive."

"You know Lord Byron—how wonderful!" exclaimed
Severn enthusiastically.

"He came to Rome about four years ago. An irascible
man, but he can be most agreeable when he's not posing.
He read to me part of the fourth Canto of *Childe Harold*—
he hadn't published it then. He pretended to be interested
in excavation, but he wasn't! He stayed only three weeks.
He went off to Venice. Now I hear he's living in Ravenna
with an Italian mistress. No morals, Mr Severn. Neither
had Count Alfieri—and both Adonises to look at. But I
believe Adonis was not exactly moral! Alas! I am talking
scandal. It's almost all that one talks here in Rome!"

Severn, a little overwhelmed, looked at this *soignée*
woman of the world of fashion. He had never expected to
sit one day on an Italian terrace and talk with someone
who had known such fabulous figures as Alfieri and Byron.

"Please—will you tell me something about Alfieri?
Did you meet him here in Rome?" asked Severn.

"Not at first. I met him in London in my father's house.
I was then a girl of seventeen—he was twenty-two, dark,
handsome, dashing. He wasn't famous then; he hadn't
written anything, I believe. We met at dances. Of course,
all the girls of my age thought he was ravishing. You
know how alluring young Italians can be with their dark
eyes, flashing teeth and beautiful manners. Then suddenly
he had to leave. There was an awful scandal. He was
caught in an affair with Lord Ligonier's wife. They fought
a duel in the Green Park. Ligonier divorced his wife and
named the Count. I didn't see him again until I was in
Paris almost ten years later, a young married woman. He
was famous then as a poet. I remember going to the production of his tragedy *Antigone* here in Rome. It was a
great social event. Everyone was there. He was the talk

of the town, not only because of his play, but because of his intrigue with the Countess of Albany—Bonnie Prince Charlie's runaway wife. A few months later we were all stunned by the news that the Pope had ordered Alfieri to leave Rome—the scandal had become too flagrant. How odd I should be telling you this here, for you can just see the roof of the Villa Strozzi where he then lived." She pointed to a red roof beyond the pergola. "Now, that's enough scandal. What about yourself? What are you painting?"

He told her, thus encouraged, of his ambition to win the Royal Academy Travelling Scholarship and to be able to stay on in Rome and study. "I must stay here. I am so happy here now!" he declared earnestly.

She liked his ardour, his youth and freshness. "You must come and see me, Mr Severn—and perhaps I can see your work? But we mustn't talk any more. Lady Westmorland's giving us a look. We are misbehaving and neglecting our partners. You say you are happy now. Why haven't you been happy before? You are young, ambitious."

"I came with a friend—who died here last February. He was more than a friend—he was a genius, greater I think than even Alfieri or Lord Byron," said Severn, earnestly.

"Now I know who you are. You are the friend who nursed that young English poet so devotedly! Everyone has heard of you! What was your friend's name?"

"John Keats."

"Keats," she repeated. "Yes—Dr Clark told me about him. Poor boy!"

Some tone of her voice evoked a memory in Severn. He looked intently at her. "I believe, ma'am, we have met before, when my friend was alive," he said. "You bought some flowers in front of the house where we were living, in the Piazza di Spagna. You dropped some of them and I picked them up. I—I——" he hesitated colouring with embarrassment as her eyes rested on his face. "I thought what a very great lady you were!"

"So it was you! I remember you now. You were most polite. How delightful to meet you here, Mr Severn. And now to our duties or we shall be dreadfully scolded!"

She turned to her right-hand partner and engaged him in conversation. A few moments later Severn addressed the lady on his left. She was very clearly English by her colouring and features, a surmise confirmed at the sight of her name-card, which was happily not obscured by the roses lying on the table, as was his other partner's. She was a Miss Fairleigh, possibly forty years of age. He found her sympathetic to talk to. She seemed to know at once that he felt a little overpowered by the company in which he found himself. There was a twinkle in her eyes, and her thin mouth had a permanent smile.

"You've been so heavily engaged that I despaired of having a word with you," she said. "Are you a newcomer to Rome?"

"Yes. I've been here only a few months. I am so sorry I seem to have neglected you, but I couldn't—I—I——" stammered Severn.

"You couldn't break away from the Dragon," she whispered.

"The Dragon?"

"We call her the Dragon—quite a pleasant dragon really," said Miss Fairleigh, smiling at him.

"You live in Rome?" asked Severn.

"Yes. I do now. Except for the war years, I've lived in Italy all my life. My father was First Secretary to Sir William Hamilton, our Ambassador at Naples. I was at Queen Caroline's Court on the day Nelson sailed in from his victory over Napoleon's Fleet at Aboukir. So you can guess my age perhaps!"

"What wonderful things you've seen!" exclaimed Severn. "You knew Nelson?"

"Mr Severn, I will be honest with you. I knew Lord Nelson, but I did not admire him. He was a great hero, but he was a dishonourable man."

She saw the expression of surprise on Severn's face.

"You are referring to Lady Hamilton?" he asked.

"No. That was bad enough, but men will be men. I knew Emma Hamilton; she was very kind to me when I was a little girl in Naples. She was beautiful but light-headed and never had a chance. Three men seduced her before she was twenty, and then Sir William Hamilton made an old fool of himself and watched Nelson cuckold him."

"Is that why you call Nelson dishonourable?" asked Severn, astonished at the note of asperity that had come into the voice of his amiable companion.

"No. That's not the reason. Mr Severn, if seducing another man's wife was considered dishonourable, then three-quarters of the men here in Rome would be dishonourable, or forgo their chief pastime!"

"But I am surprised at what you say about Nelson."

"Mr Severn, Nelson saved England and is buried in St Paul's. No man's fame is safer. *Finis coronat opus*. The world cares little about the moral deficiencies of a man who serves his country brilliantly. We all worship success, and success from which we all benefit. Nelson's heroic end blinds us to certain harsh realities. Unhappily, I was the witness of events arising from Lord Nelson's conduct that covered me with shame as an Englishwoman. But let us talk of something pleasant," she said, the smile returning to her face.

"Since you've astonished me by calling Nelson dishonourable, won't you explain?" asked Severn. "I should leave this table very perplexed otherwise."

"I see you are a serious-minded young man. Very well. I'll explain," said Miss Fairleigh. "Needless to say, I am considered quite insane on the subject. It's an episode we British are scarcely aware of, and there's no desire for enlightenment. When Lord Nelson landed in Naples that August day and the city went mad with joy—that was in 1798—the French were in occupation of Rome and the Pope had fled to Siena. On Nelson's arrival, Emma Hamilton threw herself at him in a paroxysm of hysterical rapture, as did every woman at Ferdinand's court. As you know, the King made Nelson Duke of Bronte. In November that year Ferdinand marched into Rome and three weeks later fled back to Naples in panic. He took refuge in Nelson's ship, which transported us all to Sicily along with the King and Queen, and, of course, Emma. That poltroon Ferdinand deserted his capital. He went secretly, despite the appeal of those poor Neapolitans left to French vengeance. Some of the bravest remained and later set up a republic. When the French departed, Cardinal Ruffo, now living in the Piazza di Spagna, Ferdinand's minion, besieged them, with the bloodthirsty royal troops, in the castle where they took refuge. The garrison surrendered on terms that permitted them to march out. That capitulation, Mr Severn, was guaranteed by a Turk, a Russian, and Captain Foot, our Naval representative in command of the British ship that had not gone with Nelson to Palermo. When Nelson brought us back from Palermo in June the treaty hadn't been fulfilled. Emma Hamilton was the mouthpiece of Queen Caroline, who had only one passion—to avenge herself on her republican subjects. Nelson had endorsed the terms of the capitulation and had embarked the rebels to enable them to go to France. But two days later, Emma and the King and Queen having corrupted him, Nelson handed over to Ferdinand the poor men he had embarked. The admiral of the Neapolitan fleet was summarily court-martialled and sentenced to death on board Nelson's flagship. He was hanged from the yard-arm of the *Minerva* and his body thrown into the sea like a dog's. Naples, with Nelson's assent, was given over to a Bloody Assize. The day we set foot in Naples I saw a hundred bodies hanging outside the Castle Nuovo. Four thousand were massacred. The streets ran with blood. When it was over, Nelson stayed around philandering with Emma in Naples, despite the repeated orders of his commander-in-chief to go to Minorca, for which disobedience he was censured by the Admiralty. He took his orders from those two abominable women, Emma and Queen Caroline."

"What a frightful story!" commented Severn.

"The admiral they hanged from the yard-arm was Prince Caracciolo," continued Miss Fairleigh. "He was the leader of the most enlightened and educated class in Naples. He fought with the Neapolitans when Ferdinand deserted the people, and with other patriots tried to set up a decent government. I knew him as a girl; he was a great friend of my family's. There was never a braver, more just man."

"I understand how you must feel," said Severn.

Miss Fairleigh was silent for a moment. He was aware she was struggling with her emotion, and when she spoke again, turning a sad face to him, she said, very quietly—

"Mr Severn, you are surprised that I regard Lord Nelson as a dishonourable man, despite all that he achieved for our country, even to giving his life. Now you've heard the reason for my opinion. I have one more thing to tell you, a personal one. My poor father felt so dishonoured by the whole affair that he committed suicide. My fiancé, Prince Caffarelli, aged twenty-one, who had remained and fought to the end, was among the hanged. People will tell you I have a bee in my bonnet. Mr Severn, I have!"

"If I may say so, whatever the bee, it's a very pretty bonnet you are wearing, Miss Fairleigh," he said.

"Thank you," she said, the smile returning to her face.

"Would you do something for me?" asked Severn. "I hardly know anyone at this table save my hostess, Lord and Lady Ruthven and Kirkup. Can you tell me who the others are?"

"Very well. We'll go round the table," said Miss Fairleigh. "The gentleman on my left is Prince Massimo, who owns this villa, and the beautiful little Palazzo alle Colonne. The next is Madame Apponyi, the wife of the Austrian Ambassador. Then next, Prince Barberini—I live in his palace. They say I have the salon where one of his ancestors received Milton when he visited Rome. After him, the ex-Queen of Spain, Maria Luisa, a Bourbon of Bourbons. The next I've never seen before—English undoubtedly. Then in the pretty bonnet with the lilac flowers, poor Countess Posse. Our dear Lady Westmorland is famous for her lack of tact. She alone in Rome would mix Bourbons and Bonapartes in this fashion. In fact, she enjoys these contretemps!" said Miss Fairleigh gaily.

"But are there any Bonapartes here?" asked Severn, glancing down the table.

"Three. Countess Posse is Princess Christine Bonaparte, the daughter of Prince Canino, Lucien Bonaparte, who is on the left of our hostess. The Prince is the nicest of the lot and Madame Mère's favourite son, although as a Republican he defied Napoleon and was sent into exile."

"He has an interesting face," said Severn. "But why is he called the Prince of Canino? Did Napoleon make him that?"

"Gracious, no! Napoleon never forgave him because he

married a stockbroker's widow and wouldn't give her up, not even to become King of Spain. When Napoleon arranged a match between Lucien's other daughter and that dreadful Prince of Asturias, now King of Spain, Lucien broke it off. She's now Princess Gabrielli—sitting next to Lord Ruthven."

"And Prince Canino's title?" persisted Severn, now aware that Miss Fairleigh's mind wandered a little.

"Oh, the title! The Pope gave him that. He likes him, as we all do. You must go out one day to his place at Musignano, near Canino, where he is excavating among the Etruscan tombs. He sits in a tent with an old Franciscan friar, a learned crony, directing operations. Someone rushes in and exclaims 'Eccellenza, a new vase has been found!' It's most amusing!"

"You say poor Countess Posse—why poor?" asked Severn bewildered by her sudden flights.

"Well, you see, when Princess Christine wanted to marry Count Posse, who's a Swede, there was a scene. Madame Mère and Princess Borghese wouldn't be present when the contract was signed. They objected because they said she was marrying a subject of a subject of their family."

"I don't quite understand," said Severn.

"Count Posse is a subject of the King of Sweden. The King of Sweden is Bernadotte, who was one of Napoleon's marshals, and then fought against him. So you see why Madame Mère detests the Swedes. Prince Canino is Madame Mère's favourite son, and he is expected to do whatever she wishes. So for the present father and daughter are under a cloud. What a silly world it is, Mr Severn, and so full of ill-will and gossip."

"Yes," agreed Severn. "We are almost round the table. The Cardinal with the beautiful face on Lady Westmorland's right?"

"But dear Mr Severn, you must know the most influential man in Rome! That's Cardinal Consalvi, the Pope's Secretary of State. Yes, what a beautiful head— Mr Thorwaldsen's just finished a bust of him. The French Ambassadress is next, then after Prince Canino, Lady Ruthven, Mr Kirkup, Lord Ruthven, and your partner the Dragon," she said, hushing her voice.

"The Dragon?" echoed Severn.

"That's our name for the Duchess of Devonshire, Queen of the Bluestockings," whispered Miss Fairleigh. "Where are you staying, Mr Severn?"

"I have a little studio in the Via San Isidoro," he answered.

"Write it down in my book. I will give you my card. You must come and see me. I will ask a few people in to meet you. Perhaps Mr Thorwaldsen? He's a dear friend of mine."

She produced a small book and a gold pencil. He wrote down his address. Judging from the magnificent rings on her hands, she must be a rich woman. He was a little dizzy with all she had poured forth. The last information had been the most astonishing. That he should be sitting next to the Duchess of Devonshire and have talked with her, ignorant of her identity!

There was a movement at the table. Lady Westmorland and the Cardinal had risen. They led the company to a lower terrace with a baroque fountain and masses of purple bougainvillæa. Footmen appeared with coffee and camomile. Severn was addressed by the Englishman, the one person unknown to Miss Fairleigh. He introduced himself, a Mr Williamson of Edinburgh. He had been travelling in Italy for three months. He expressed the greatest interest in art. That morning he had called on Prince Piombino and had seen the fresco, *Aurora driving away darkness* by Guicino, also the famous statue, *Ares*, the

God of War. "Beautiful! Beautiful! exclaimed Mr Williamson, offering Severn a pinch of snuff. "They found it in the portico of Octavia, who was Marc Antony's wife, I believe. Just think of it! And what beauty here!" He waved his hand in the air. "But also what filth everywhere else, my dear sir! Fleas in the beds—biting you at the dinner-table too! My partner was scratching herself all through lunch. Says the fleas never leave her alone— cruel, cruel!"

Mr Williamson took another pinch of snuff, peered over his glasses and said in a whisper: "Very embarrassing to drive through the streets with a lady—the things they do here in corners; often not in corners. Disgusting, disgusting, and in the centre of Christianity! Of course you cannot blame the Pope. No, sir. A beautiful character. I was received by him yesterday morning on the introduction of Abbé Taylor of the Scots College. Most gracious! I'm a Presbyterian, four generations strong, but I was impressed. What do you think His Holiness said to me?" Mr Williamson gave a chuckle, tapped his snuff-box, and continued: "He told me that when he first came to Rome he could remember only one chimney here. Now he can count one hundred. He says they are all due to British residents, who won't winter here without fireplaces! I don't blame them! There was an American gentleman received with me—wanted to kiss the Pope's toe. The Pope wouldn't let him. Must have been a devout Catholic, but isn't it very contradictory, coming from a country that advocates the absurd doctrine of equality at birth? Otherwise a very sensible fellow, from Cårolina, where, I understand, they're not such hot republicans. He told me, by the way, that some of the States have just agreed to abolish slavery—bound to lead to trouble one day, he says. Have you travelled much in Italy, sir?"

"Hardly at all," answered Severn, amused by this

garrulous little man. "We came by boat to Naples and then on to Rome."

"Oh, how wise. What trouble you missed! I am travelling with an accomplished and invaluable friend who is much distressed by the inconvenience of our journey."

"Which way did you come, sir?"

"I shipped my carriage from Ramsgate to Ostend, and then on through Bruges and Cologne. Hotels very poor, not yet recovered from Boney. Have you a profession, sir, or are you travelling for pleasure?"

"I am an artist, studying here. I came with a friend— who has since died," answered Severn.

"How very distressing! So you are an artist! That, sir, is the most admirable of all callings. I am somewhat of a connoisseur. Perhaps you will do me the honour of calling on me, sir? Intelligent conversation upon the arts is always much to be desired. I have rooms in the palace of Prince Canino—who has kindly brought me here and introduced me to our hostess. What a beautiful woman! What grace and wit! She informs me that it was in her London drawing-room that Lord Byron met Lady Caroline Lamb—rather a disaster for 'em both, eh?"

Mr Williamson laughed, tapped his snuff-box and proceeded:

"Prince Canino has an admirable gallery. I am fortunate to see it. His collection isn't shown, as the family inhabit the rooms where it is hung. There's a portrait of the Duke of Urbino by Raphael, and *Modesty and Vanity* by Leonardo da Vinci. Speaking of that great man, have you seen the collection belonging to Cardinal Fesch— Napoleon's uncle? Really remarkable, sir."

Mr Williamson turned at the sound of footsteps. It was Lady Westmorland, accompanied by Cardinal Consalvi. She presented them both to the Cardinal. Mr Williamson gave him a most profound bow. Severn looked with intense interest at the handsome face of the man who was considered the ablest member of the Sacred College. Severn had been long enough in Rome to learn of the bitter ecclesiastical feuds, the scandals, the simony of the Church. No one could live here unaware of its opposition to reforms, its feudal tyranny, its Papal gaols and the galleys groaning with chained victims. Yet many spoke well of Pius VII. Severn had seen him one evening walking near the Coliseum. The Pope's carriage, a crazy-looking machine, drawn by six horses with postilions in purple livery, followed behind him as he slowly walked with his gentlemen. He was dressed in a scarlet mantle, a broad-brimmed scarlet hat edged with gold, and stockings and shoes of the same colour. As he came towards him, Severn uncovered and bowed. The Holy Father made his sign of benison, and gave him a warm smile. Severn had been deeply moved, conscious that here were embodied nearly eighteen hundred years of an unbroken Christian tradition. He recalled that when Napoleon arrogantly said to this Pope, "I am the successor of Charlemagne and though your Holiness is the Sovereign of Rome, I would have you know I am Emperor of Rome," he had replied, undaunted: "Your Majesty makes a mistake. You have crowned yourself Emperor of the French, not Emperor of Rome. There is no such person." What he had suffered at Napoleon's hands! He had shut himself up in the Quirinal Palace when the French troops established themselves in Rome. Then Napoleon's General Radet, like a thief in the night, had broken into the Quirinal and carried him off into exile for three years, deprived of secretaries, gentlemen and even writing materials. Now when Severn looked on the beautiful face of the Pope's Secretary of State, he again, as on that day near the Coliseum felt a similar emotion. It was like looking on the face of history.

"Mr Severn, I saw you deep in a *tête-à-tête* with Miss Fairleigh," said Lady Westmorland, after the presentations. "I fear the Duchess must have felt quite out in the cold!"

She spoke with a smile, but he felt the reproof.

"I am so sorry, Lady Westmorland," he said.

She tapped his arm with her fan and laughed. "You are quite forgiven. There is only one lady more dominating than the Duchess, and that's Miss Fairleigh." She turned to Cardinal Consalvi. "These gentlemen are students of art, Mr Williamson is a connoisseur. Mr Severn is Mr Thorwaldsen's favourite pupil."

"Then he is in excellent hands. I have recently been one of Mr Thorwaldsen's subjects, a very flattered one, I fear," said the Cardinal with a smile. "I asked him to make me a little more stern and he wouldn't. He told me he had annoyed Lord Byron by refusing to make him look disagreeable. What a strange ambition! One has to do so many disagreeable things hoping one won't look disagreeable."

"Your Eminence, Miss Fairleigh so much desires to be presented," said Lady Westmorland, moving.

"Certainly," responded the Cardinal as she led him away.

"Alas! I am not a connoisseur, despite Lady Westmorland's kindness," said Mr Williamson in a tone that made his renunciation an acceptance.

"Mr Thorwaldsen would be astonished to learn I am his favourite pupil—I have not yet met him and I study painting not sculpture," exclaimed Severn, laughing.

It was three o'clock when the guests departed. In the hall Kirkup came up to him.

"I saw you crushed between the Dragon and the Cobra," he said as they left the villa.

"I found the Duchess of Devonshire very pleasant,"

replied Severn, "but Lady Westmorland rapped me for neglecting her."

"Yes, quite pleasant, despite her nickname. She has three passions. The Proprieties, having been improper, Excavation, and Cardinal Consalvi," remarked Kirkup.

"Improper—but how?"

"Too long a story after so good a lunch, my dear Severn."

"Miss Fairleigh—the Cobra. Who is she?"

"She is the *Roman Intelligence*, but without intelligence. Her brain is a pea rattling in an empty skull. She's very nice, inexhaustible, and quietly venomous, with the smile of a seraph. She's Rome's most assiduous pervert."

"Pervert?"

"Our nickname for the converts. She's gone over to Rome three times, and has come back twice. Did she say anything about Nelson?"

"Yes. I happened to ask about him," replied Severn.

"*Dio mio!* Then I'll wager she went off like a rocket. No *nil nisi bonum* about the Cobra!"

"I thought her story a very sad one," said Severn. "Aren't you a little severe on her?"

"Perhaps I am; but other people have had unhappy love affairs when young. I hope I won't be permanently embittered by mine," he said.

Severn looked at him sharply. He saw that his companion was quite serious. They walked in silence for a few minutes. When Kirkup spoke again he said quietly, "I understood so well what your poor friend Keats suffered."

Severn knew then the meaning of Kirkup's comment on Miss Fairleigh. It was the first and last time that he alluded to the shadow over his own life.

II

A few days after the luncheon at the Villa Negroni, Severn was invited to lunch by the Duchess of Devonshire, to dinner by Lord and Lady Ruthven and was called upon by Mr Williamson, who took him to see the pictures at Prince Canino's. He found him indignant because the British Consul had charged him two crowns for hiring a naval lieutenant's uniform.

"But for a fancy dress that's not dear. In London you pay a guinea," said Severn.

"It was not for a fancy dress. It was for my audience with the Pope!"

"You are in the Navy, sir?" exclaimed Severn, astonished.

"No. You should know, Mr Severn, that for an audience with the Pope one must wear a uniform or full evening dress. Evening dress in daylight is very drab, so the British Consul has a naval lieutenant's uniform that he hires out—but I protest against paying two crowns to hire a shabby uniform. They say the Pope smiles privately. He has seen it so often."

Severn burst into laughter. "As I shall never have an audience, I shall never have to wear it, but I think it should be an admiral's at least," he commented.

Mr Williamson took a pinch of snuff and closed his box with a snap. A few minutes later he made another complaint. Prince Canino was charging him too much rent. There was no night porter. The gates of the Palazzo were firmly shut at nine o'clock. He had to hammer and hammer and then tip a surly servant.

"The nobility are indolent and poor. It is folly to trust to their honour. Never, Mr Severn, never take a suite in their palaces without a written agreement, with every detail defined. And their morals! With a *cavaliere servente* sitting at every wife's toilet table! And the priests! Everyone is employed and controlled by the Church. No one can live otherwise. Nor does it make for a pious or honest community. It is unsafe to be in the streets at night. There have been four murders in them this week. Sir, I shall be glad to see Edinburgh again!"

They mounted a wide staircase to the *piano nobile* from the mezzanine floor where Mr Williamson had his suite. An old, shabby footman conducted them to the gallery and opened the shutters for them to see the pictures. The gallery ran round two sides of a courtyard with palm trees and a grotto with water cascading over tiers of ferns and baroque figures.

They were halfway down the gallery when a gentleman entered at the far end and advanced towards them. He was accompanied by two young ladies. Severn recognised him as Prince Canino. He greeted them most affably and presented them to his daughters. When he had done the honours he conducted them to a salon hung with beautiful tapestries, and ordered wine. Since Mr Williamson did all the talking, Severn had an opportunity for studying Napoleon's brother, a remarkable man in every sense. He had outraged Napoleon by two *mésalliances* and, worse, by his republican sympathies. He had married first Christine Boyer, an exquisite creature but of low birth, whose portrait by Gérard hung in the gallery. His second choice had been a stockbroker's widow, Madame Jouberton. Two marriages for love were too much for the Emperor. Moreover, the tiresome fellow had refused two thrones! He could have been King of Naples or Grand Duke of Tuscany on condition that he got rid of his wife and took an available Infanta. He stoutly refused and went into exile at Rome with Madame Mère, who agreed with him. This rebellion had produced Sir Walter Scott's jibe: "A Frenchman refusing a crown and declining to part with his wife is indeed one of the most uncommon exhibitions in an age fertile in novelties."

Prince Canino had two passions, archæology and astronomy. He interrupted Mr Williamson's dissertation on the School of Raphael and, in excellent English, spoken also by his daughters, began to talk of his excavations. He went over to a cabinet and took out an Etruscan vase of great beauty, one of a collection of two thousand, and also a gold bracelet, which he fastened on to his elder daughter's arm.

"It may have been worn by a princess or queen. It came out of one of the Royal Tombs and is probably over four thousand years old," he said, the collector's pride shining in his eyes.

Presently the daughter wearing the bracelet, Princess Gabrielli, engaged Severn in conversation, which somehow turned to music. The two sisters were very animated.

"We prefer Scotch music," said the Countess Posse.

"I am greatly flattered!" exclaimed Mr Williamson, appropriating the remark as directed to him. "Will not your Highness sing a Scotch song for me?"

"We will both sing!" declared the Countess vivaciously, going over to the piano.

They sang very well. After three songs they delighted Mr Williamson with a most spirited rendering of *Scots wha ha'e wi Wallace bled*.

"Now where, may I ask your Highnesses, did you learn that—and so admirably sung?" asked Mr Williamson.

The young ladies laughed. "Ah, that is a secret, monsieur!" said the younger sister.

"I shall betray them!" cried their father. "They have a priest who comes in from the Scots College—to which your Prince Charles Stuart gave his sword and the buckles of his shoes—to teach them music."

When Williamson and Severn took their leave it was five o'clock. The prince and his daughters accompanied them to the grand staircase.

All the way down it, Severn's mind was trying to comprehend the incredible change in his circumstances. Here he was in Rome, a poor and unknown artist visiting the brother of Napoleon in his palace and having his daughters sing for him! A few years ago he was an engraver's apprentice sleeping in a back room in a little street in London. What a story he would write home to his people!

"It's difficult to believe, is it not, that that charming young lady—I allude to the Princess Gabrielli—might be sitting on the throne of Spain had her father permitted it," observed Mr Williamson sententiously.

Severn started out of his reverie. "The throne of Spain?" he repeated.

"Indeed, Napoleon commanded her to marry the Prince of Asturias. She was only a girl of fifteen. Her father consented reluctantly, and then when she was about to leave for Madrid he declared that he couldn't condemn her to such a life. The poor girl was distraught by the very idea. The Prince of the Asturias, now Ferdinand of Spain, sir, is without doubt the most contemptible monarch in Europe to-day, even more so than his namesake in Naples. What an escape for that dear young lady! I have the whole story from the Abbé Taylor of the Scots College."

Mr Williamson shook Severn by the hand and stood at his door until he had descended to the street. A pompous bore, and yet a rewarding bore, reflected Severn. For he had given him an excellent lunch, a most enjoyable afternoon, and had commissioned a drawing of Raphael's skull on exhibition in the Academy of St Luke—which Thorwaldsen declared to be a fraud.

CHAPTER VI

I

THE glory of May passed. In the first week an extraordinary story had circulated through the salons of Rome. Some believed it, others scoffed at it. Every time that Severn went past the palazzo on the corner of the Corso, with its veranda overlooking the Piazza di Venezia where Madame Mère and Cardinal Fesch dwelt in seclusion, he thought about the strange incident that had happened there on the fifth of May. The windows of the Palazzo Bonaparte, as it was now called after its occupant, looked on to the former Embassy of the Venetian Republic, and also on to the Palazzo Torlonia, where the banker gave his dazzling entertainments. He was considerate enough when a ball took place there to have his windows kept shut in order that the noise of the orchestra and the revelry should not disturb Madame Mère across the Piazza. Malicious gossip said it showed great consideration to a competitor in business, for Madame Mère, thrifty, having conserved her wealth derived from the glamourised business of wholesale murder, made profitable loans. She financed the derelict Bonapartes now gathered under her wing in Rome. Thrift had been a habit her son could not cure. "You must see more company, befitting your rank, *Ma Mère*," said Napoleon.

"Then give me two millions instead of one, for I must save; it is my nature," she retorted.

The watchful Metternich in Vienna was nervous of Madame Mère. Her income was too large. The Austrian Ambassador reported that if His Holiness found himself in need of money he had recourse either to Torlonia or to

Madame. There was irony in the fact that when the
Austrian Emperor had proposed visiting Rome the apart-
ments designated for him had been furnished by a loan
from Madame Mère to the Pope.

An air of mystery hung over the Palazzo Bonaparte.
The exiled Emperor's mother gave no parties. She was
seen to drive in and out of its cavernous entrance porch
attended by her small court. All the Bonapartes in Rome
were in awe of her. They were summoned from time to
time and instructed or admonished. Her relations with
the Vatican were influential to the degree that she
caused the Pope to make a plea to the Prince Regent of
England on behalf of the prisoner on St Helena—in vain.

The speculation upon what had transpired within the
walls of the Palazzo Bonaparte, where Madame Mère
hoarded her gold and Cardinal Fesch his rich collection
of pictures, reached fever point in the last week of May
when a story related in the salons of Rome provoked a
battle between the credulous and the incredulous. The
debate had created a riot in the Caffé Greco. Ewing
almost quarrelled with Kirkup, and Overbeck was deeply
offended because Severn told him he was capable of
believing any nonsense. "Yes, nonsense," said Severn,
firmly.

"Absolutely true!" declared Mr Williamson, who had
the story direct from Prince Canino.

It transpired that on the afternoon of the fifth, at
twilight, a stranger, dressed wholly in black, called at the
Palazzo Bonaparte and asked to see Madame Mère.
"Madame receives no one who has not requested through
her chamberlain an audience," he was told.

"It is absolutely necessary that I should see Madame
Mère at once," he replied.

The porter hesitated and then conducted the stranger
upstairs to an ante-room. Here, questioned on his business,

he refused to give his name, but insisted on seeing Madame Mère "on most important business which must be told to her alone." His manner was so impressive that his message was delivered. Madame Mère consented to receive him and he was conducted into her presence by her chamberlain. He bowed low on entering the room where she sat with her ladies-in-waiting. He requested that he might speak to her alone. At her order they withdrew. Then, in a grave voice the strange visitor said, "While I am addressing your Highness, this very hour on St Helena, the Emperor, your son, is freed from his sufferings. He is dead," he said. Taking from his bosom a crucifix, he held it towards her, adding, "Kiss the image of the Redeemer. Be of good faith. You will meet again after some years. You will rejoin him who was the source of such profound sorrow to you. But before that much will happen in France. Blood will flow, there will be civil wars, Europe will burst into flame as in a conflagration."

He spoke with all the solemnity and certainty of a prophet of God, and before Madame Mère, stunned by this pronouncement, could recover, he went, silently, never to be seen again. The next day all Rome was searched in vain for a clue to this mysterious visitor. For some days Madame Mère was prostrate from shock.

When Severn passed the palazzo he often saw her carriage waiting under the portal. Once he lingered, and presently was rewarded by a glimpse of the old lady as she drove out accompanied by two ladies. She was of medium height, and had a regal air. There was determination in every line of her face. Married at sixteen, the mother of thirteen children, at seventy the vestiges of a handsome woman of patrician bearing were still visible in her brilliant dark eyes and fine features. Here she was regal in a sense that none of her sons and daughters had been. Between them they had occupied six thrones. All of them were now dispossessed, while Madame Mère reigned in Rome by sheer force of character.

By now Severn was acquainted with the leading figures in Roman society, thanks to Lady Westmorland. She had taken command of him and had him frequently at her table or by her side in her carriage when she went out to make calls. The more he saw of her the more fascinating and astonishing she was. No other woman, not even the Duchess of Devonshire or Lady Compton, both of whom had salons to which all Rome flocked, rivalled her in her brilliance as a conversationalist or in her incredible energy. A fluent linguist in four languages, a good musician, sparkling in company, she dominated her circle, though few could have said she was loved by it. Her wit was of a rapier quality whose thrusts could leave wounds. She was utterly unpredictable in her habits and turned night into day. Her parties seldom concluded until the dawn came over the city. It was quite usual to call and find that her ladyship had not arisen at six in the evening. She was invariably late for every invitation she accepted, and arrived like a *prima donna*, creating an air of ovation around her. Considerable wealth enabled her to maintain a large household run in the greatest style, with English and Italian butlers, maids, footmen, grooms, gardeners and a retinue of visiting ministrants; the dressmaker, coiffeur, music-master, drawing-master, secretary, doctor, the Franciscan or the Dominican alms-collector, all waited in her ante-chamber for audience as though at the court of a queen. An heiress in her own right, separated from her elderly husband, she knew no restrictions.

She showed the greatest kindness and interest in Severn and his work. It flattered her to think that as a patron she could encourage art, on which she was prepared to talk at great length but with small discernment. She brought to Severn's little studio relays of her friends. There were times when it seemed as if visiting his studio had become one of her entertainments. Her carriage would draw up at all hours, creating a small sensation with its liveried coachman and footman, its air of extravagant elegance. She would descend from it, regal in bonnet and shawl and billowing silk, her voice high-pitched but musical as she closed her parasol and ascended his stairs. The footman preceded her to announce her advent and ensure that Severn was at the door to receive her.

"And now, Mr Severn, what have you to show me to-day?" she would ask, seating herself near his easel. That her seat might be dignified and comfortable she had sent him a beautiful Louis Seize chair. "For your patrons," she said. But he knew it was for herself. Forty-one, the mother of four sons and two daughters, whom she never mentioned, she was still a beautiful woman, her bright colouring enhanced by her lovely eyes and a perfectly formed mouth. She treated Severn with a touch of raillery, never condescending and yet always keeping him aware that she was a great lady, a peeress of England, a leader of society. She did not choose to define her interest in this extremely handsome young man at her beck and call. She persuaded herself that it was a kindly interest in a deserving young man of talent. Gossip did not ascribe her interest to art as much as to the artist. It was pleasant to have an agreeable, complaisant and attractive young man in attendance even if that was all.

For his part, Severn's attitude to her imperious ways was not without self-interest. He realised early that she was a woman who could easily take offence, who would brook no opposition and who would make a formidable enemy. Her social rank opened doors for him that he never could have entered and took him into a world of affluence and good manners. It was a world also in which he found patrons whose commissions were essential to his existence.

The parties at the Villa Negroni were always superb entertainments. Throughout that spring her guests lunched or dined on the wide terrace drenched in the scent of orange blossoms. Lady Westmorland had a gift for impromptu excursions. One evening, very late, she ordered carriages and transported her guests to the arena of the Coliseum. Here she had arranged for the choir from the Sistine Chapel to sing while invisible in the arches. Another excursion was made at midnight to the vast Baths of Caracalla, where a small orchestra in a roofless hall played excerpts from Rossini's *The Barber of Seville*, at whose première in Rome Lady Westmorland had been present, on the occasion when it was hooted from the stage. The following year she had been at the première of *La Cenerentola*, being by this time an ardent admirer of the composer. He was present at her dinner party on the night of the excursion to the Baths of Caracalla, and what had appeared to be a spontaneous suggestion during dinner proved to be a carefully rehearsed compliment to Rossini, who went with the party. She was prolific in devising such unusual entertainments.

Severn's circle of acquaintances within three months of Keats's death had become large and diversified. Everyone liked him. He was gay, adaptable and very handsome. Many feminine eyes were turned in his direction, but he remained fancy-free, much to Elton's amazement. For him the Princess Borghese affair had come to an end. "You know Severn, she's a bore with her incessant craze to be adored. You can't play Romeo without a little time off. Also, she's too old for the Juliet rôle." But Severn knew of another reason. A niece of Lady Compton had been in Rome a month and he was deeply smitten with her virgin charm.

No one knew that Severn's immunity was due to his overwhelming anxiety about his work. He had no time or taste for philandering. *The Death of Alcibiades* slowly growing on the canvas monopolised such time as he saved from attendance on the dazzling Lady Westmorland. Where was Lord Westmorland, he often wondered. Only once had she mentioned him, calling him "That impossible husband of mine." Severn felt embarrassed.

He made other friends besides those met at the Countess's table. One morning in the Capitol Art Gallery he was copying Rubens's *Romulus and Remus*, for which he had a commission, when an elderly gentleman stopped by his easel. Presently he made a few complimentary remarks which led to a general conversation. In a few minutes Severn found that he must be talking to a man who seemed to know everyone, unless he was romancing. The stranger spoke of Sir Joshua Reynolds, who often dined with him, of Dr Johnson, to whom as a young man he had been taken by Boswell, of William Wordsworth, who had stayed with him at his country seat, of Wilkie, the artist, from whom he had commissioned *The Blind Fiddler*, and of Sir Walter Scott, who had met Sir Humphry Davy under his roof. Severn told him that he had studied at the Royal Academy School under Fuseli, had won the Gold Medal, and was now hoping to win the Travelling Scholarship.

"Then perhaps you know young Edwin Landseer?" asked the old gentleman. "He was a student there. I bought from him a picture of some fighting dogs when he was sixteen. That was some two years ago—a gifted boy."

"I met him the first day I went to the Life Class, sir," answered Severn. "Fuseli put us both to drawing the feet of Hercules."

He liked this genial, aristocratic old gentleman who confessed to his own passion as an amateur artist. He wore clothes of an old-fashioned cut, but a man of wealth and taste was indicated. Presently he glanced at his watch.

"It is almost noon. I know of a quiet restaurant nearby. I wonder if you would give me the pleasure of lunching with me that we might continue this enjoyable talk?" he asked with charming courtesy.

Severn flushed with pleasure. "Indeed you are most kind, sir," he replied. "It would be an honour."

"My name is Beaumont—Sir George Beaumont of Coleorton, Leicestershire," he said, putting forth his hand.

"My name, sir, is Joseph Severn."

They lunched in a restaurant that had been built into the vaults of part of Trajan's Forum. It had a long garden with a vine pergola and a fountain. Everywhere, it seemed to Severn, there were fountains. They brought a coolness to the air, a flash of silver, a gentle tinkling music, and by night their voices increased in volume as the streets fell silent.

Sir George was a perfect host. He had a manner of inviting confidence and very soon Severn had told him the whole story of events that had brought him to Rome. His host showed the greatest interest.

"One of the things of which I am most proud," he said, "is that I was fortunate enough to recognise the genius of Mr Wordsworth, who has often been my guest at Coleorton and has written there some memorable inscriptions for my gardens. Perhaps you will lend me the book of your friend's poems? There is no pleasure so great as the apprehension of young genius, Mr Severn. Yesterday, I visited Mr Gibson's studio—a young man of great promise. He had a delightful model in clay of a statue, *Psyche borne by the Zephyrs* that I commissioned in marble last year. My visit to Rome this year is memorable for one purchase I have made. I've bought an unfinished bas-relief of *The Virgin, Child and St John* by Michelangelo which I shall present to the Royal Academy. It's my intention to give the whole of my collection at Coleorton towards a National Gallery, which surely we should have!"

Sir George talked of a dozen things, and in the warm noonday over a bottle of good wine Severn listened enchanted. It was three o'clock when they rose from the table. Severn realised that his day was ended, for the Gallery closed at four, but he counted the time well lost in such an encounter. On leaving, Sir George suggested that they should go into the Forum.

"I promised the Duchess of Devonshire to visit the Column of Phocas, which she excavated a few years ago. She tells me it never quite disappeared through all the centuries and was the only one visible in the actual Forum. No one knew what it represented until she dug down twenty feet and found that it had been erected to the memory of the Emperor Phocas. The Duchess showed me a lovely little chalice they came upon during the excavation."

They walked across to the Forum and found the column, rising from a pit below the level of the meadow on which cattle were grazing. It was fluted and of beautiful proportions.

"I'm told that it was originally put up by the Emperor Diocletian, commemorating the great fire of A.D. 282," said Sir George as they walked around the base and read the inscription on it. "How history repeats itself! In 1666 we had the Great Fire and put up a column in the City to commemorate it—larger, but not as graceful as this. Phocas appropriated this column and for centuries its origin remained a mystery until the Duchess dug it out and found the inscription. She told me a very odd thing. Lord Byron was here four years ago, working on the fourth canto of *Childe Harold*. In that poem he mentions the column and calls it 'Thou nameless column with a buried base.' But the odd thing is that when he saw it—if he ever saw it—it wasn't buried and it was no longer nameless, for the Duchess had unearthed it a year earlier! Well, we are all fallible! Homer nods!" exclaimed Sir George.

"Do you know Lord Byron, sir?" asked Severn. "He lived opposite our rooms in the Piazza di Spagna, I'm told."

"Yes—but slightly. I once met him at one of Mr Samuel Rogers's breakfast parties in St James's Place. I wonder, Mr Severn, if you are free for dinner next Friday evening? Mr Rogers is dining with me. A small party."

"Indeed, sir, it would be a very great pleasure," responded Severn eagerly.

"I have an apartment in the Palazzo Altieri. On Friday, at eight, then?" said Sir George as they parted.

So another exciting day in Rome had passed. What a pity he didn't keep a diary, thought Severn, when he got back to the Via San Isidoro. He found a letter awaiting him on his table. The envelope bore a coronet. Inside there was a note in Lady Westmorland's handwriting: "On Friday we are dining at Lord Lansdowne's. I shall call for you at eight."

The note filled him with dismay. He knew how much Lady Westmorland disliked having her arrangements upset. Her commands were regal, her temper fragile. He wrote four notes before he was satisfied that he had expressed his regrets as delicately as possible. He had it despatched to the Villa Negroni at once.

The next morning about eleven o'clock, while working on his picture, Severn heard the familiar sound of a carriage drawing up below his window. He looked out and saw Lady Westmorland descending from it. She was dressed more flamboyantly than ever, in a pea-green bonnet with flowing ribbons, and velvet spencer and cambric frock.

Severn went to the door and awaited her. At a glance he saw that she was displeased.

"Mr Severn," she said as soon as she had seated herself, "I am distressed about Friday. Lord Lansdowne is a great friend of mine. He is forming a collection for his town house and at once I thought of you and procured you an invitation. Now you tell me you can't come. It makes me look very silly!"

"I had already made an engagement which it is difficult to break. I am most sorry, your ladyship."

"Cannot it be put off?"

"Alas, no," responded Severn.

"With whom is your engagement may I ask?"

It was on his tongue to snub this infringement of his liberty, but he restrained himself. She had been very kind to him and was a person of very great influence here in Rome. It would be disastrous to quarrel with her.

"I'm sorry if I have inconvenienced your ladyship. You are always so kind in thinking of me. Yesterday morning I met Sir George Beaumont, who——"

"That old bore!" exclaimed Lady Westmorland.

"I found him most interesting. He very kindly asked me to dinner on Friday to meet Mr Samuel Rogers. I naturally accepted."

"What a pair of old dodderers!"

"Mr Rogers is the famous author of *The Pleasures of Memory*," said Severn.

"Have you read it?"

"No."

"It's rubbish!" said Lady Westmorland firmly. "He's nothing but an old snob from a banking counter, masquerading as a man of letters."

"Lord Byron ranks Mr Rogers above Mr Wordsworth and Mr Coleridge."

"Lord Byron's opinions, like his morals, are unpredictable!" retorted Lady Westmorland. "If you *will* enter into engagements with anybody who invites you then I shall find it very difficult to promote your interests, Mr Severn."

"I most greatly regret any inconvenience I have caused your ladyship. You are always most kind," said Mr Severn as she rose to go.

He escorted her down to her carriage. As she was about to go she tapped him on the arm with her fan. A curl of his dark hair had fallen over his brow. In his distress he looked even more handsome, she thought.

"We are not going to quarrel, Mr Severn. You are new to Rome and you will learn in time to avoid tedious engagements. *Arrivederci!*"

She gave him a regal smile, proud and beautiful, as she drove away. She left him all that day out of tune for his work. But the next day he received an invitation to go to Frascati with her on Sunday. She was going to lunch with Prince Canino, who had a villa, La Rufinella, at Frascati. It was famous for its gardens and baroque fountains and grottoes. "The Prince is delighted you are coming. He remembers your visit to his gallery with pleasure. The Princesses will be there," wrote Lady Westmorland.

It was at once a command and a sign of forgiveness. Happily, he had no other engagement for Sunday. He too remembered that visit to Prince Canino's with pleasure, and particularly the princesses who had sung *Scots wha ha'e wi Wallace bled.*

The dinner party at Sir George Beaumont's on Friday night was a success that at one moment seemed likely to be a disaster. It was a small company of six, all gentle-men of whom Severn was very much the youngest. Mr Samuel Rogers was there and also Mr Williamson, who was attired in a wonderful gold-and-blue embroidered silk waistcoat that made him shine like a parrot, to which he had a singular resemblance in many respects for he had a large nose, talked incessantly and preened himself.

Another of the guests was Prince Henry of Prussia, the youngest brother of King Frederick William. He lived in Rome, and was a celebrated character of whom Severn had heard the strangest stories from the Bunsens. He was a recluse who seldom went out to parties. He disliked the daylight and lived in a villa whose shutters were never opened until sunset. It was said that he dined only three times a week; on the intermediate days he took nothing but strong coffee and dry bread. His servants were in-structed to remain invisible, on pain of dismissal, until he rang for them. When he gave dinners he listened to the conversation with close attention, but rarely uttered a syllable. Yet he was a gifted linguist and a man of con-considerable learning. His time was mostly spent in read-ing newspapers, for he was a parlour politician and kept himself abreast of affairs by reading the German, French, English, Spanish and Italian journals. He employed a secretary whose chief task was the clipping out, pasting up, and indexing of paragraphs he had marked. Re-nowned for his liberality, everyone who had ever been in his service received a pension. It was said that twenty of these pensioners lived in his villa along with a horde of cats all decorated with blue collars and bells. He was a recluse in his house for three months at a time and then suddenly had a fit of walking. These excursions were always taken in the summer between twelve and three, when all Rome was at its lunch or prostrate with heat and the streets were silent and empty. It was said that he had called on only two persons during all his years in Rome —Herr Niebuhr, the Prussian Minister, and Cardinal Consalvi, the Secretary of State. He never succeeded in finding the energy to be received by the Pope.

Another member of the party was an English clergyman, chaplain to Lord Lansdowne. He told them that his Lordship had spent £180,000 in two years on statuary, pictures and books for his collection at Bowood.

The dinner was excellent and beautifully served. Sir George, a perfect host, drew each member of the company to contribute to the conversation. Severn, somewhat overwhelmed by the standing of the guests and the nature of the diverse subjects discussed, was mostly silent. Mr Williamson, as usual, was full of historical allusions and critical opinions, and made an attempt to display the breadth if not the depth of his interests. He was soon challenged by Mr Rogers and each time went down in defeat, but nothing deterred him. The Prince turned a baleful eye on the protagonists.

At the end of the dinner they ascended to a loggia on the roof of the villa. It afforded a magnificent panorama of Rome and the mountains beyond. The night was warm and starlit. There was a moment when the conversation turned upon the struggles of artists and writers. Sir George referred to a timely legacy from a friend which had saved Wordsworth from journalistic drudgery.

"Our young friend here can tell us of a poet who was not saved from such drudgery."

"What poet was that?" asked Rogers.

"John Keats," said Severn.

"Oh, yes. I remember that name. He twice wrote asking me for money."

"I am very sorry, sir, but that cannot be correct. Keats would never ask anyone for money," said Severn in a voice that did not hide his indignation.

"Oh yes, he did—like all the others! I'm never free from begging letters. I've helped dozens of poets," said Rogers stubbornly.

"Mr Rogers, you may think me rude, but I cannot allow you to defame my dead friend in this manner," said Severn, flushing with anger. "There is no basis whatever for such a statement."

There was an embarrassed silence.

"I beg your pardon, sir," said Severn, turning to his host. "I have no wish to create a scene, but I cannot hear my dead friend traduced in this fashion and not raise my voice in his defence."

"It does you credit, Mr Severn. I am sure Mr Rogers means no offence," said Sir George, turning towards the banker-poet. "Mr Rogers has played Mæcenas to so many literary men that it is quite possible he may be confused in this instance."

The guests all looked at Mr Rogers. He seemed in no way perturbed. He turned to Severn calmly.

"I apologise, Mr Severn. I was somewhat careless in my statement. You are quite correct. Your friend Keats never applied to me for assistance."

"Thank you, sir, for that withdrawal," said Severn.

The sudden storm died away, the conversation turned agreeably to a new opera of Rossini's and then to the story of Madame Mère's mysterious visitor. Some mention was made of Napoleon's little son, the Duke of Reichstadt. For the first time that evening Prince Henry spoke.

"I've seen the child," he said laconically.

There was a pause and the company waited for the Prince to continue. But he did not continue. After a prolonged silence, Sir George turned to him and said, "I am sure everyone would be glad to hear something about the child, your Royal Highness."

The Prince seemed to contemplate for a few minutes,

bending forward in his chair, eyes on the table. Then he sat up and spoke slowly: "I visited the Emperor Franz in Vienna three years ago, and saw the little King of Rome, as he was then called. A few weeks later they deprived him of that title and renamed him the Duke of Reichstadt. He is a beautiful child with a mass of flaxen hair. He had much character in his face for a boy of seven, but I could see little resemblance to his father. He is a Hapsburg in appearance. I was much attracted by the little fellow. He was very bright and had beautiful manners, which he owes to a devoted French governess, Madame de Montesquiou. But they are trying to bring him up a Hapsburg. He can speak both German and French, but he often chooses not to speak the former. The child clings to the memory of his father, despite the attempt to turn him into a good Hapsburg. They've dismissed Madame de Montesquiou. I think they are wrong and they may fail. The chaplain at the French Embassy told me that when Méneval, Napoleon's former secretary, who had accompanied his mother to Vienna, was dismissed and went to say goodbye to the child, he felt a tug at his coat as he bowed, and the little boy whispered, "Monsieur Méva, you will tell Papa that I still love him dearly." Méneval burst into tears. Think of it, the child was then only four years old, and hadn't seen Napoleon for fourteen months! I wonder what the end of the story will be when the little King of Rome becomes a man, and what history will say of us. I am not happy about what we are doing to that child."

There was a long silence after the Prince had spoken.

"I hear much criticism of the Duchess of Parma," said Mr Williamson, breaking the silence.

"The woman is worthless. She should take her child and join Napoleon on St Helena," said Prince Henry, a note of passion in his voice for the first time.

"If the Allies would allow it," remarked the chaplain.

"Sir, if they would not allow it they would be damned by history," exclaimed Prince Henry. He was silent for the rest of the evening.

At midnight the party dispersed. As Severn was leaving the hall, Samuel Rogers came towards him and placed a hand on his shoulder.

"I hope I am forgiven, young man. I have a very weak voice. If I did not say ill-natured things no one would hear me. I am often ashamed of myself, but I fear I'm incurable," he said, offering his hand.

"Your apology is very handsome, sir," said Severn, shaking his hand. "We are none of us immune from that failing."

Severn thanked his host and said good night. "I hope, sir, I am forgiven?" he asked.

Sir George looked at him, a smile on his benign face. He held Severn's hand between his own as he answered:

"There is nothing to forgive, there is much to admire, Mr Severn, in your defence of your friend. For Mr Rogers, of whom I would not have you think unkindly, despite this regrettable lapse, I would say this—or rather Mr Campbell the poet has said it: 'Borrow five hundred pounds of Rogers and he will never say a word against you till you want to repay him.' Good night, my young friend. Next week my wife and I go to our villa at Tivoli. It would give us much pleasure if you could visit us for a few days. There we can talk at length of the things that delight us."

Overwhelmed with the old baronet's kindness, Severn accepted the invitation. All the way home through the silent streets his heart was singing with youth's joy of life.

II

In July Severn's painting was finished and despatched. It would be just early enough to reach London for the sitting of the Academy Council. After a lapse of two weeks he was appalled to learn that it had missed the boat at Civitavecchia owing to an agent's blunder. Lady Westmorland, arriving at his studio, found him in the depths of despair.

"You must not worry," she said. "All is not lost yet. Sir Thomas Lawrence is a very good friend of mine. I shall write to him and explain what has happened through no fault of yours. He can let the Council wait for its arrival before making any award. Everything will be all right and you will win the prize. We all think your painting is admirable. I shall tell Sir Thomas that. I'll be leaving for Lucca on Tuesday until the middle of August. You must keep me informed of what happens."

Most of the English colony had already left Rome in advance of the summer heat. Severn joined a small band of fellow artists who were spending the month of August at Subiaco, an artist's paradise in the Sabine Mountains. Just before he left, news arrived of the death of Napoleon on St Helena. It had occurred on the very hour and day of the mysterious visitor to the Palazzo Bonaparte. Madame Mère at her summer villa at Albano went into deep seclusion. Princess Borghese collapsed and took to her bed. "Life has no longer any attraction for me, and all is at an end," she wrote to a friend.

Towards the close of August Severn received an invitation to join Lady Westmorland, who had arrived at Civitavecchia, where she had taken the British Consul's villa on the seashore. After a brief halt in Rome, he journeyed there. The weather was glorious, the evenings cool. There was a house party of ten, among whom Lady Westmorland was the most vivacious and tireless. She rode, she swam, and played faro long into the night. She never appeared before noon. Severn employed his time reading and working on a miniature of Lady Westmorland. He experienced one of those swift and light love affairs that take their tone from the soft and dramatic Italian landscape. She was an English girl of twenty-two, just out of a convent school in Brussels, the daughter of one of Wellington's generals. She was coquettish and teased Severn. For two weeks he was deeply in love with her until Lady Westmorland informed him that, being very well-born and an heiress, she would make a very good match. He knew she was warning him, and he kept his feelings in hand. Jane Fawcett left, and it was obvious that the artist had made no lasting impression on her. There was one persistent cloud over that happy month of *dolce far niente*. No news came of his picture. They returned to Rome at the end of September.

Lady Westmorland was seized by a new idea. Egypt was again open to tourists. An English professor of Egyptian hieroglyphics, Dr Young, passing through Rome, filled her with a sudden desire to visit a "civilisation older than Rome's." Dr Young had succeeded in deciphering the names of Ptolemy and Berenice on the Rosetta Stone discovered by the French in 1799. Soon it might yield up its meaning and reveal a new world of Egyptian lore. Lady Westmorland began to astonish her friends by babbling of "the cursive hieratic" and the "cursive demotic," greatly enjoying the bewilderment on their faces. Suddenly it became imperative for her to go to Egypt. One afternoon she called on Severn at his studio. She had arranged to meet Dr Young in Cairo, she said. Here was a wonderful opportunity for him to study Egyptian art and paint the Egyptian scene. Of all the artists in Rome, she felt that he was the most suitable to profit by such an excursion. He would come with her as her guest.

Dismayed, Severn pointed out that he had a number of commissions in hand that he could ill afford to neglect. Moreover, it would be unwise for him to go so far afield while he was awaiting news of his scholarship painting.

"Surely, Mr Severn, you cannot hesitate. There will never again be such an opportunity. Of course you will come! Those commissions can wait," she said.

"Your ladyship, much as I appreciate your kindness, it is impossible for me to go," he replied.

"Impossible! Nonsense! Nothing is impossible if one has the will!" she cried, her eyes angry at his refusal.

"I don't think your ladyship appreciates my position. If I do not gain the scholarship, I must return to England. In that case I must go with an adequate portfolio of sketches of the Roman scene for my future work."

"You are just being obstinate, Mr Severn!" said Lady Westmorland, unused to being opposed in any whim.

"I am sorry. There is another reason also. A young Academy friend of mine has just arrived in Rome. We have arranged to take a studio together. I could not disappoint him," explained Severn.

"There is no need. Why could not your friend come too, as my guest?" asked Lady Westmorland.

He could hardly hide his surprise at this offer.

"That is most generous of your ladyship. May I suggest that Mr Catherwood should go in my place, if you approve of him?"

Lady Westmorland made no reply for a few moments. Then she rose from her chair and looked into his eyes. All her sudden anger seemed to have vanished.

"You are a very obstinate young man, Mr Severn! Bring your friend to me early to-morrow evening. I am going later to the French Ambassador's Ball. I don't think you realise what a tantalising person you are," she said with a playful smile. Then with a sudden sweep of her hand she ruffled his hair and laughed at him in her musical voice.

When she had gone Severn went to his window and

looked out on the rosy evening sky in which the small Roman swallows were criss-crossing. His brow was damp with perspiration. It had been an ordeal to oppose her— a dangerous ordeal, for she was a woman of sudden and intense likes and dislikes. She was quick to imagine an offence or even persecution, and she could be ruthless. His whole career here in Rome could be jeopardised by her just as quickly as it had been made. And he was troubled also by an apprehension to which he hesitated to give a name. "The woman's in love with you," had said Kirkup, teasingly, one day. "Be careful, sweet boy!"

He had laughed at this foolish idea. He knew now it was not so foolish. He must be very careful or he would be overwhelmed with disaster.

III

Henry Catherwood, newly arrived in Rome and excited by a scene so full of colour and sunshine, was not enthusiastic when Severn explained why they were going to call on Lady Westmorland. Egypt, of which he knew nothing, held no attractions, and what little he had heard concerning Lady Westmorland made him still less inclined to embark on such an adventure. He was a simple young man of quiet habits. Anything that suggested going into Society frightened him. He had been friendly in London with Severn, where they had met at the Royal Academy classes. A small legacy had enabled him to spend a winter in Rome. He had been delighted when Severn had suggested that they should take a studio together.

Since Severn had committed him to calling on Lady Westmorland, he let himself be taken to the Villa Negroni. A footman showed them up to the salon on the first floor, whose ceiling had been decorated by Peruzzi with the *Loves of the Gods*. He felt slightly embarrassed by the nudity and liberty of their raptures, and was amazed to learn that a sixteenth-century Cardinal had commissioned the decoration. They had ample time to study the ceiling. Three-quarters of an hour passed before Lady Westmorland entered the salon. She was an amazing vision of gleaming snow-white shoulders and bosom. She wore an Empire gown, high-waisted, daringly *décolleté*. Her beautiful throat was encased in a pearl collar and she wore a diamond tiara with long ear-drops to match. She carried an enormous ostrich feather fan. Her shoes were gold and her dress glittered with silver sequins on a blue lamé ground. Never had Severn seen her so excitingly beautiful.

Lady Westmorland advanced towards them with the smooth grace of a swan, and apologised for keeping them so long. She had been dressing for the ball that evening at the French Embassy. She bade them sit down, and rang for refreshments. Severn saw at once that she was in a mood of melting graciousness. In a few minutes she had put his nervous friend at ease and charmed him by the vivacity of her talk. She outlined her proposed trip to Egypt, the things she had planned to see. At a first glance she liked this simple young man who had an air of quiet distinction. There was nothing bohemian about Mr Catherwood. She hated bohemians.

Within half an hour, subjugated by her beauty, charm and wit, all Catherwood's opposition to the Egyptian excursion had vanished. Severn was astonished to hear his friend say that he could think of nothing more exciting than visiting Alexandria, Cairo, the Pyramids and Philæ. When at last she dismissed them it was practically settled that Catherwood should go as her guest along with Severn, for she had it firmly in her mind that they were both to accompany her. In despair, Severn uttered no protest, yet he was determined not to go.

When they departed Lady Westmorland went down to

I

her carriage, which had been waiting for an hour. She gave them a ride as far as the Piazza Barberini and engaged them for dinner the next Saturday night. Severn was dismayed to find that Catherwood had completely changed his mind. He could think of nothing more wonderful than to journey to Egypt with such a brilliant hostess, and to make that trip in the greatest possible luxury, with a bevy of servants and dragomans. Severn remained firm in his determination not to go. His scheme for making Catherwood his deputy had failed. Somehow he must devise an escape without antagonising the lady.

It troubled him for two days. And then the problem was settled for him. Lady Westmorland appeared draped in heavy black from head to foot. Her dearest aunt had died very suddenly. It was a very great shock and she was almost prostrate. She could not possibly think of making the trip to Egypt now. It must be postponed until next year. "But we will go next year, and both of you will be my guests," she said graciously, turning from one to the other as she rose to leave the studio. They escorted her down to her carriage and were astonished to find the grooms wearing large mourning bands and the horses' heads decorated with black plumes.

"What will she do when she buries her husband?" asked the disappointed Catherwood when her carriage with its five horses had gone.

"Go into white and gild the horses' hooves," replied Severn.

He had expected the dinner at the villa on Saturday would be cancelled, and when he had mentioned this she replied, "Oh no. I still want you both, but it will be most *intime*."

When they arrived at the Villa Negroni they found that there were eighteen guests for dinner. Lady Westmorland appeared in a dress of white tulle with red roses in her corsage. An orchestra came in after dinner and they danced. She had completely forgotten her dearest aunt and the wonders of Egypt.

One morning Severn received news from London that plunged him into despair. His picture had arrived and then it had been lost somehow between the forwarding agent and the Royal Academy! It was the end of all his dreams of the scholarship, of his sojourn in Rome. Lady Westmorland, calling, found him on the verge of a nervous collapse. She rallied his spirits, promised to write again to Sir Thomas Lawrence, who couldn't refuse her anything, and assured him that she would procure enough commissions for his miniatures to see him through his troubles.

"The young Duke of Devonshire arrives next month. I shall make him buy your picture of Alexander. He is enlarging the gallery at Chatsworth. He is very rich and a patron of all the arts. There is no need for you to worry, Mr Severn."

He continued to worry. Late in October came the news that the picture had been found at last, damaged, in a tin trunk in the Royal Academy's basement. Again Lady Westmorland gave him comfort. It was not possible that he should be penalised because of the carelessness of the Academy. She would see to it that he was not.

His work suffered. He abandoned a picture commissioned by Sir John Drummond. His thoughts these days turned to his dead friend, whose grave he regularly visited. One day he found Mrs Bunsen there, placing flowers near a small headstone, and he learnt that while they were at their summer place last July her infant daughter had died. As they left the cemetery she pointed to a small gravestone and said: "Three summers ago the little son of Mr Shelley, the atheist poet, was buried there. I said then it was God's punishment for his evil life. How wicked and un-Christian of me, Mr Severn! We refused to call on them when they were here, as did others in the English colony. Why are we so cruel to each other? Poor man, I know his sorrow now!"

It was singular that within a week Shelley, whom he had met in those wonderful days when he went with Keats to Leigh Hunt's hospitable home, should come into his life again. One morning he received a package, much delayed. It was a small book entitled *Adonais*. With it there was a letter from Shelley asking his acceptance of it. When he opened the book and read the Preface the tears came into his eyes. There was a tribute in it to himself, referring to his last services to Keats. Presently he read the poem. It was an elegy for his friend, every line inspired. He read it twice, overwhelmed, and then, more composed after the transcendent emotions it evoked, he turned again to the Preface. As he re-read it all the deep depression and anxiety in his soul these last weeks was lifted. He knew now, come what may, that his life had not been in vain. There was one paragraph that sounded like a trumpet call. He picked up a piece of charcoal and on the wall of the studio he wrote Shelley's tribute to his devoted attendance on Keats:

"*May the unextinguished spirit of his illustrious friend animate the creations of his pencil, and plead against oblivion for his name.*"

When Catherwood came in later he found Severn hard at work on his picture. Then he saw the writing on the wall and slowly read it.

"Who wrote that?" he asked.

"I've written it, but the words are the words of a poet as great as my friend Keats—Percy Bysshe Shelley. If ever I am remembered, it will not be for my paintings but for those words," said Severn.

Catherwood was about to make a comment but he kept silent. There was a wonderful radiance on the face of his friend.

CHAPTER VII

I

IN the month of December two bright scions of the young Republic of the West arrived in Rome, Mr George Bancroft and Mr Joseph Coolidge. They were both Harvard products, eager and intensely ambitious. One of them, Mr Bancroft, sat in his room in the Hotel Colonna, a few yards out of the Piazza di Spagna, having just returned from a walk on the Pincio, where he had watched the sunset over Rome. He was now writing up his Diary. This Diary, so carefully kept since he had left Boston one June morning three and a half years ago, narrated many experiences. He had set forth on his travels, being scarcely eighteen, in the most serious mood, sustained by the sum of seven hundred dollars a year provided by the President of Harvard College, from which he had graduated with high honours. This munificent allowance was given to him so that after an accumulation of knowledge gathered in centres of ancient learning he might fulfil his intention of entering the ministry.

The Diary recorded that in August, 1818, he was at Leyden in Holland. The University of Göttingen had been his goal, and there he lingered until March, 1821, sitting at the feet of learned professors until he had received the degree of a doctor of philosophy. His Diary further recorded that the boy-doctor had called on Goethe at Weimar. He was most courteously received by the old poet, who could not be drawn to discuss other German poets but expressed admiration for Byron's *Don Juan*.

From Weimar he went to Heidelberg, stayed six weeks and then pushed on to Paris, arriving early in May. The next day, the Diary recorded, he met Washington Irving, "Very amiable and altogether unassuming." The following afternoon he presented himself to the celebrated Baron Humboldt, who took him to a session of the Institute of France. They arrived at a time of crisis in its history. The most learned assembly in the world was in full session. Wishing to honour the memory of Descartes, the philosopher, it had voted him a funeral, collected his bones, neglected for over a century and a half, walked in solemn procession to the new grave and there deposited them. Alas! some ribald persons had declared that these were not the actual bones of Descartes, that the teeth were not the genuine teeth, etc. All Paris was laughing at the Institute. So now they had gathered to hear the celebrated Monsieur D'Alembert prove to the assembly at great length that these were indeed the bones of Descartes which they had solemnly conveyed to the new sepulchre.

On May 29th, recorded the Diary, he had met America's famous ally and soldier, General Lafayette. He had stayed on in Paris, enjoying the company of Washington Irving, "the most amiable and excellent man, in so far as I may judge, whom I have met with in Europe." There had been some perturbation at this long sojourn in Paris, but he wrote home reassuringly: "You are right to warn me against the vices of Europe. Yet as far as I have been in the world I find one place nearly as bad as another. I mean by that, there is everywhere the means of indulgence offered to the dissolute. The number of dissolutes is, of course, unequal. But after all, is Amsterdam worse than Hamburg, or is Paris worse than Amsterdam? And can Naples exceed Paris? He that will be vicious can be so in any part of Europe." Surely that reply had disposed of parental fears?

From Paris he had gone on a walking tour through the Alps, bound for Italy. Their solitary grandeur promoted solemn thoughts. "It seemed to me that my disposition fits me for a clergyman," he wrote.

A little later, one October morning, Bancroft entered the enchanted portal. Italy spread her treasures before him. In youthful rapture he visited Milan, Venice and Florence. Something flowered within him, putting to flight his New England Puritan austerity. He bought a pair of lavender trousers, a blue satin waistcoat and a frilled shirt. He entered Rome on November 25th, and went early next morning over the Tiber bridge, past the Castle of St Angelo, to St Peter's, which quite overwhelmed him.

Well-introduced, enthusiastic, of good address, he had just come of age. Doors opened readily for him. On December 21st a door of the Palazzo Borghese opened. He went in nervously and came out hypnotised by the charm of the Princess Pauline Borghese. "She has a more elegant suavity of manners than I remember to have seen in any woman of rank," he recorded, oblivious of the fact, a steady democrat, that this was the first woman of rank, the first royal person, he had encountered.

Princess Borghese received him privately at first. She was delighted by his boyish embarrassment and freshness. After a few questions about his home in America and the length of his stay, she showed him her collection of diamonds and precious stones, exhibited in a *cinquecento* cabinet. Then they passed into a vast salon hung with the works of Italian masters, and rich with tapestries. From the painted ceiling great chandeliers of crystal carried innumerable lighted candles. The Princess greeted some fifty guests assembled there. Young George Bancroft discovered they were mostly Italians drawn from Rome's aristocracy. There were a few English and French present. Halfway through the evening a young Italian went to the piano and seated himself, but before the music began the Princess caught Bancroft by the hand.

"Come!" she said, smiling at him. "You must meet my

sister-in-law, Madame Patterson Bonaparte. She's a countrywoman of yours. Perhaps you know her?"

He did indeed know her. Madame Bonaparte had fought a desperate battle for her rights for seventeen years. In 1804 Napoleon's youngest brother Jerome, on his way home from the West Indies, had taken refuge from the British fleet in the United States. There he met and married lovely Elizabeth Patterson, the twenty-year-old daughter of a Baltimore merchant. Napoleon, being about to proclaim the Empire, was furious. He ordered his brother home and refused to recognise the marriage.

Since it had been solemnised in the Catholic church the Pope refused to annul it. Napoleon defied the Pope, and annulled it. Young Prince Jerome hurried home to plead with his brother, who proved obdurate and gave orders that Jerome's wife should not be allowed to set foot in Europe. Madame Bonaparte sailed to join her husband and was not permitted to land at Lisbon and Amsterdam. She proceeded to England. In a Camberwell lodging she gave birth to a son, Jerome. The father wrote vowing fidelity to his wife and bade her to wait. She waited for two years, then she learned that Prince Jerome, dragooned by his brother, had married a German Princess and had been made King of Westphalia. He had the effrontery to suggest that his discarded wife and son should come to Westphalia and he would make her Princess of Smalcald. She indignantly refused his offer, as also Napoleon's offer of a pension of 60,000 francs if she would give up the Bonaparte name.

Since the day of her marriage she had persistently claimed her rights as Prince Jerome's lawful wife. Now, seventeen years later, she had arrived in Rome with Jerome's son and had succeeded in being received as Mrs Patterson Bonaparte by Madame Mère and Princess Borghese.

Bancroft, familiar from boyhood with this *cause célèbre*, was therefore astonished to find Mrs Patterson Bonaparte a guest in Prince Borghese's palace. The bad faith of her two brothers did not appear to embarrass the Princess, who now introduced her with cordiality.

It was two in the morning when he left, his head swimming as he went down the marble staircase of the Palazzo Borghese. Torches flared in the sconces on the walls. In the courtyard, above the sound of the hooves of restless horses, he heard the splash of water coming from a great stone grotto overlaid with ferns. He hesitated under the high archway leading into the street. A carriage halted and an English voice said, "Can we take you home, Mr Bancroft?" A groom jumped down from the box seat and opened the door of the carriage for him. He entered. In the dim light he saw a lady, her throat flashing with diamonds. A young man sat by her side.

"I am Lady Westmorland—we talked during supper."

"Oh yes—it is most kind of you, ma'am," he answered.

"This is Mr Severn," said Lady Westmorland. "He is studying art. Are you studying here, Mr Bancroft?"

"No, ma'am. I am preparing for the ministry," he answered.

"How interesting! My stepson, Lord Burghersh is a diplomat."

"I mean a spiritual ministry, Lady Westmorland."

There was a pause.

"That's most interesting. Where can we take you, Mr Bancroft?" she asked.

He gave her his address. He could now see that her companion was a young man, extremely handsome. He inquired about his work and learned that he was an artist.

"You must let me take you to Mr Severn's studio," said Lady Westmorland.

He thanked her. Before he arrived at his destination, she had arranged to call for him the next morning at twelve, to visit Mr Severn.

All that had happened three days ago. He had seen Mr Severn's paintings and had bought a copy in miniature of Raphael's *The Deposition*, most beautifully executed. It stood now before him on his table. He had found Lady Westmorland beautiful, charming, witty, but somewhat frightening in her possessive manner. To-morrow, Christmas Day, he was to lunch with her at the Villa Negroni. His social list grew rapidly. Next week he was dining with Princess Borghese. It was all very exciting, but was he becoming too worldly?

Throughout his tour he had kept his Diary faithfully. Until he had come to Rome it had been a record of his studies, but now it had become a chronicle of social engagements. Lady Westmorland had taken him up. She was a fascinating woman, but what would the President of Harvard College think of her? She was scarcely the kind of person he would have found rewarding. And Princess Borghese?

A little perturbed, he read over what he had written, then he glanced at his watch. It was nearly seven o'clock. He had an appointment with Joseph Severn at the Caffé Greco, where artists, writers and musicians of every nationality gathered. He got up from the table, changed into his lavender trousers, bought in Milan, and a blue coat just delivered from a Roman tailor. It was very fashionably shaped at the waist. He carefully tied a yellow cravat that went well with a green embroidered waistcoat and gilt buttons. Then he selected a pair of pointed leather shoes made for him in Paris. Taking a muslin handkerchief, embroidered with his initials, he opened a bottle of scent and sprinkled it. Finally, a gold-topped cane and glossy beaver hat in hand, he surveyed himself in the mirror with approval. He would have caused much surprise in Boston and Harvard, but he was in Rome and here you did as the Romans did, with certain reservations.

The Caffè Greco was but a few yards distant, in the Via Condotti. In the evenings it presented a scene of great gaiety. It was already famous when Goethe resided in Rome and for over a year had gone there with his artist friends, Tischbein and Angelica Kauffmann. Canova became a figure there and later Thorwaldsen, the young Danish sculptor who speedily won fame. The artistic youth of Europe coming to Rome regarded it as one of the sights. They thronged the little tables in its small successive salons with frescoed walls. Under a pall of thick smoke they drank and talked until the dawn came up and the sun's early rays caught the cross on the great dome of St Peter's.

Entering it this Christmas Eve, the elegant young Mr Bancroft found the Caffè crammed, buzzing with voices and noisy with scurrying waiters and the clatter of china. A dozen debates in various languages seemed in progress. The dandies, bohemians, sculptors, painters, musicians and dilettantes mingled in every kind of dress, from the flamboyant elegance of the well-to-do to the negligent attire of the struggling artist. Bancroft walked down the low rooms searching for Joseph Severn. He had not arrived and as he stood looking for a place in which to sit, Severn's friend, Seymour Kirkup, hailed him and offered him a seat at a crowded table.

"My dear fellow, if only you'd come a few minutes earlier! You want to meet Rossini. He's just gone out with Isabella Colbran. I heard her last night at the Argentina, in *The Barber of Seville*, his new opera. Wonderful! She sang like an angel. They're off to Venice. There's a rumour he's going to marry her. Have you seen Severn? We're all waiting for him."

"I've come to meet him—he said seven o'clock," answered Bancroft, as a place was made for him at the table.

"Mr Westmacott, Signorina Bruno, Mr Gibson, Mr

Catherwood, Miss Julia Walker, Miss Maria Walker—nieces of Lord Elgin" said Kirkup in an aside, "and Mr Eastlake," he concluded, introducing him to the company. Bancroft was about to sit down when suddenly a young elegant, a youth of his own age, rushed across to the table and from behind flung his arms around him.

"George! How wonderful! What are you doing here? How long have you been here? I'd heard you were in Italy!" said the youth jubilantly.

Bancroft stiffened a little under this ecstatic greeting. Joseph Coolidge, his ardent handsome friend, came of one of the best Boston families, and was a Harvard colleague, but he felt a little embarrassed by this excited greeting in the presence of strangers. Before he had answered the questions poured on him, Kirkup, ever gracious, had invited Coolidge to join their table.

"Most kind of you, sir!" responded Coolidge genially. He bowed to the company before seating himself. Very handsome, very young, and eager, he smiled at them all. Signorina Bruno and the two Miss Walkers smiled back at the young Adonis who had descended on them. In response to Bancroft's questions, he gave them a full and enthusiastic account of his progress through Europe. Unlike his friend, he had not pursued learning; he had frankly enjoyed himself. He had been away from home two years. Last year in Rome he had seen Thorwaldsen's bust of Lord Byron and was not happy until he had bought a copy of it from the sculptor. Then he had journeyed to Ravenna to call on his lordship, armed with an introduction from Washington Irving.

"He was wonderful!" exclaimed Coolidge in reply to their questions about the great poet. "I was paralysed with emotion—to see him, to talk with him! It was a dream! He was so kind, not one bit like what so many say—and all I had hoped he would be, magnificent-looking, a lord, a great poet in every inch. I wonder what he thought of me bursting in on him like that!" exclaimed Coolidge, with his ingratiating smile.

"I, too, have a letter to Byron from Washington Irving. Now I shan't be afraid to present it," said Bancroft.

"Can't you take us all?" asked Maria Walker.

"I'd love to take you, and I'm sure Byron would love to see you, Miss Walker," responded Coolidge gallantly. He smiled at her. She was about his own age, and the beauty of her colouring captivated him. Her younger sister was also lovely to look at. English roses in Rome. He wondered who they were, if they were staying here long.

"What's happened to Severn? We want him very particularly," said Kirkup. "Don't we, Westmacott?"

"Yes. We've got a Christmas box for him," answered Westmacott.

The company demanded what it was. He shook his head. Only Kirkup and Westmacott were in the secret.

Severn was late. He had three miniatures on hand, and since he needed the money badly he wanted to finish them. He worked on by candlelight, although he knew it was tricky for the colours. On his easel was a half-finished painting of *Alexander and Diogenes*. The young Duke of Devonshire was coming to Rome, and Lady Westmorland thought he might be induced to buy. He was a lavish patron of the arts, collecting for his great house in Derbyshire.

This was Severn's second large canvas, the successor to his ill-fated *Death of Alcibiades*. There was still no report on it from the Royal Academy. He had lost all hope. The travelling pension would never be his; if he stayed on in Rome he would be doomed to a hand-to-mouth existence, to the endless production of miniatures of society women. That was not art as he conceived it.

He worked on, absorbed, and then, looking at his watch, was perturbed to find that it was almost seven o'clock. He was due at the Caffé Greco, where he had arranged to meet George Bancroft, the pleasant young American whom Lady Westmorland had brought to his studio three days ago. Kirkup had been there. He liked him and had suggested this evening's rendezvous. There was someone else who would be at the Caffé, a friend of Kirkup's who knew everyone in Rome, Maria Walker, whom he had met with her sister at his rooms a week ago. He had been embarrassed on being introduced to her. She had exclaimed: "So you're the remarkable young man! We wondered who you were almost a year ago. Julia said she thought you were one of Canova's models! Mother was sure that you were English."

"Your mother was right. But why was I remarkable?" Severn had asked, recovering from his embarrassment.

"Oh, we thought you remarkable because—oh, because——" She hesitated, and the blood mantled her cheeks, deepening the colour in them.

"I could never doubt that you are English, Miss Walker. You've been a year in Rome?" Severn had inquired.

"Oh no. Mother has a villa at Naples. We have just returned," she had replied.

When Severn entered the Caffé Greco he had a boisterous welcome and was relieved to find that Bancroft was sitting with his friends. He apologised for his tardiness. It was pleasant to see Miss Walker again.

"May the remarkable young man sit near you?" he asked, jokingly, bringing up a chair.

"You're never going to forgive me for that, are you?" cried Maria Walker, making room for him.

He found an elegant young American, Mr Coolidge, at his left.

"It is a great pleasure to meet you, sir. I have long desired it," said the youth in the bottle-green coat and waistcoat. "Posterity will never forget your services to John Keats."

Severn looked at him startled.

"You have heard of Keats?" asked Severn, surprised.

"Indeed! I met Mr Shelley in Pisa last summer. He lent me a volume of Keats's poems, telling me that he had died here a few months earlier. And now I hear how devotedly you nursed him. May I come and talk to you about him, about his poems?"

For a few moments Severn did not answer, and when at last he spoke young Coolidge saw he was deeply moved.

"How strange—that you should know of my poor friend and that you should know Mr Shelley! Yes, please come to see me—43, Via San Isidoro—any morning."

The waiters had placed a bottle of wine and glasses on the table. Richard Westmacott, a student of sculpture under Thorwaldsen, and the son of a Royal Academician, filled the glasses, stood up, and then raised a glass.

"Ladies and gentlemen, this is a Christmas Eve toast—but it is something much more," he said. "This morning I had a letter from my father—reproving me among other things for being overspent, just as he always was when he studied here, I'm sure! I said 'among other things.' It's one of those things that are really important. Severn, you can't raise your glass to this toast, for we are drinking to you as the winner of the Royal Academy Travelling Scholarship and its representative here. So, ladies and gentlemen, success to our friend Severn!"

They all rose with a scraping of chairs and a raising of glasses that drew attention to their table. Severn sat dumbfounded. So the news had come, and all the anxiety haunting him this last ten months was at an end. It was difficult to realise his reprieve from this nightmare that had hovered over him. Now he could stay in Rome, no longer harassed by anxiety about commissions. He had a pension of one hundred and thirty pounds for three years, and eighty pounds travelling expenses. It was opulence. Above all, it was recognition. He sat dazed by the news, and then somehow found words to thank these good friends of his.

"So you *are* a remarkable young man!" laughed Maria Walker as he sat down.

"Thank you, thank you—my work doesn't really deserve this," he said apologetically.

But it was not his work she was thinking of. It was his face, his eyes, alive with such sensitive beauty. If he had been the writer of poems, Keats not Severn, she would not have been surprised.

Three days later the mail brought him confirmation of the news. With it came a covering letter from Sir Thomas Lawrence, President of the Royal Academy, congratulating him. To his surprise, the Academy had also paid the expenses of his journey to Rome. Now he would be able to furnish his shabby studio. He would be able to do lots of things, among them to send his mother and his father money for new clothes. He would send his married sister Sarah ten pounds to help with the rent of her little house in Goswell Street where he had lodged in his student days. He would send five pounds to Maria for a new coat and bonnet, and a pound to young brother Charles with which to buy music.

II

Mr Bancroft had much to record in his Diary, but, alas! the pressure of events was sadly interfering with his entries. There was the kindness of Seymour Kirkup, who had invited him with Severn to a Christmas dinner at his beautiful studio overlooking the private grounds of Prince Borghese's park. He had a large terrace on to which the studio opened, with a magnificent view across Rome to St Peter's and the pine-crowned Janiculum Hill. The next day Kirkup had procured him admission to the Casino Borghese. It was not inhabited. The Prince, having quarrelled with his wife, lived at Florence. The Princess, after many wanderings, had gone back to the Palazzo Borghese. She pursued every stratagem to get her husband brought back to Rome, not because she loved him, but because she liked to annoy him. It fretted her to think that he could be happy with his mistress. Bancroft walked through the vast salons of the Casino where Cardinal Scipione had housed his great collection of antiques and old masters. Many of these were missing. At a price that was a virtual theft, Napoleon had forced his brother-in-law to surrender them and had taken them to Paris. "Canova recovered for the Pope many of the things filched by the Emperor from the Vatican galleries," explained Kirkup, "but nothing has been done for the Prince. The Pope, when a prisoner of Napoleon's, passed through Piedmont, of which Borghese was Governor. He's not forgotten how Borghese snubbed him."

Half-empty, the great Casino in its superb park was still a magnificent house. Bancroft wondered how the Princess Pauline, with whom he had dined the previous evening, could be content not to live in it, despite the splendour of her quarters in the Palazzo Borghese. And what a magnificent setting she had there, and what a glorious woman she was! Oblivious of the truth about her, his Puritan and democratic instincts overwhelmed by the glamour of her personality, he had written home an account of his visit with all a boy's enthusiasm, dazzled by her graciousness towards him.

Now while the sun poured down into the hotel

K

courtyard below him, with its vine pergola and dolphin fountain, he opened his neglected Diary and read its last entry, made on January the first:

The new year has opened most beautifully. A warm sun, a cloudless sky, a mild refreshing air filling my heart with gladness: a pleasant thing it is to the eyes to behold the sun: to me the earth seems beautiful. I love life.

He would not alter a word of that. He was young, healthy, in Rome. His future promised infinite happiness. How brief, how sad the lot of others! Two mornings ago, on the request of Coolidge, Severn had taken them out to the Protestant Cemetery to visit the grave of Keats, the liveryman's son dead at twenty-five, a poet of genius, according to Coolidge. The cemetery was a miserable open piece of ground near the Aurelian Wall. A place for heretics. His New England blood stirred in indignation.

He began to write in his Diary, bringing it up to date:

Rome, January 5, 1822.
In the evening to Princess Pauline Borghese where I introduced Coolidge. We entered the palace just before eight, and were glad to find only the Princess's own family collected. She soon made her appearance, sweetly dressed, arrayed in beauty and smiles and received us most graciously. We formed a little circle round her, and she guided the conversation with a most winning sweetness of manner. I have never known what she is till now; for now she spoke of herself with ease and freedom, mentioned her own misfortunes, her predilection for the United States, saying they were the only asylum for persons who had suffered as she had.

She spoke of her health, which is wretched; that she had grown wan and thin; and yet even in her ill-health she is beautiful. She can eat nothing—so weak is her stomach; and for the whole day had taken only a little bouillon. She sees company though she is fond of solitude, for her ill-health inclines her to melancholy.

She said all this with great gravity, made us observe how small her waist was, how thin her arms, which used to be large and round: showed us her ornaments, new articles for her toilette just received from Paris; chatting now like a moralist of her misfortunes and now like a woman of her beauty and ornaments. Fêtes she does not long for, for of fêtes she had had enough under the Emperor.

All this was said with such grace and sweetness that we could not but feel deeply for her. Though a fallen princess, she still presumes her dignity fully: she is the centre of conversation; the mistress of all present; she bids one to remove a table, another to sing, another to dance and everyone loves to be the first to obey her. Without any requesting it she called for her tablets and wrote me a card of entrance to the little villa which she has been building in the environs of Rome, and which is reckoned very pretty.

The Princess receives from Prince Borghese twelve thousand dollars per year, which is, I should think, hardly enough to support her establishment; for her palace is vast; and she is unaccustomed to economy. Her toilette, I think she said, cost four thousand dollars. The Princess seemed to think it quite impossible for a lady to dress for only six hundred dollars a year: and a hundred and twenty guineas were nothing for a lady's toilette. And so to-night I believe we saw the Princess in all forms; in all, too, she seemed the most graceful, elegant and well-bred woman I have ever seen.

We had some delightful music—"nothing but music does me good"—and the Princess seemed delighted as a divine air was sung deliciously. We left the palace a little after ten, and were quite delighted with our evening and most particularly gratified that the Princess had received us on an evening when there was no company with her. Her niece, a daughter of Louis, the ex-king of Holland, was in the room, and her eyes were of a black glossy beauty that might produce an effect on young hearts.

I came home and wrote some verses—The Complaint of a Princess *which are hardly worth copying into this journal. Went to bed a little after two o'clock.*

Bancroft put down his quill. There was a sharp tap on his door. He rose and opened it. Coolidge stood there in magnificent array. He wore tight-fitting nankeen pantaloons strapped down to his shoes, a scarlet embroidered waistcoat and a russet velour jacket. His throat was swathed in a large yellow cravat. A glossy beaver surmounted his curls.

"This is luck! I've come to collect you. I've a carriage downstairs and in it the two most beautiful girls in Rome, also Severn, and a luncheon basket. The day's gorgeous. We're going to picnic in the Campagna. We want you!"

"Who are the ladies?" asked Bancroft cautiously, eyeing his friend with envy. He would never dare to dress like that.

"Maria and Julia Walker. Somehow Severn's persuaded them to come along with us."

"I'll come, but I must change," said Bancroft.

"Good! I'll go down and tell them. Hurry up!" cried Coolidge.

A bright lad, reflected Bancroft from the lofty superiority of one year. He was sorry that he would soon lose his debonair friend, for he was going south to Naples in the last spring of his European life. Coolidge was going north.

He selected his attire very carefully. He would not be outclassed in the matter of dress. He put on his powder blue coat, fashionably skirted and cut in at the waist, and wore a white shirt with a frilled front. A loose blue cravat with a large cameo, bought in the Via Condotti, completed his attire. He gave himself an approving glance in the mirror, and then went down to join his friends. He had only one thing marring his happiness—the ceaseless prodding of a New England conscience. He felt he was slipping into a worldly condition. It alarmed him, he wrote to a friend in America, that "sweet Italian is interceding for utterance, when I should in decency talk nothing but plain English."

CHAPTER VIII

I

SEVERN no longer awoke every morning with anxiety about his future preying upon his mind. With an assured income for three years, small though it was, and the prestige of having won the Academy Travelling Scholarship, his buoyant spirits revived. One success followed another. Lady Westmorland was untiring in her efforts to promote his interests. He found himself with more commissions than he could fulfil. It became a vogue to have a miniature or a picture by young Mr Severn. He was aware that to his art he could add the asset of his personality. It would have been hypocritical to pretend that art achieved all. The ladies who sat for their miniatures derived as much pleasure in looking at the artist as he derived from studying them. It happened also that his style was somewhat flattering to his sitters. The pleasure with which he looked at life was reflected in the faces he painted.

It was also a consequence of these commissions that young Mr Severn was invited to the soirées, dinners, theatrical entertainments and excursions in the country that occupied the time of the English visitors. He was so agreeable, so handsome and gallant, so full of infectious enthusiasm for everything. As his paintings became more and more in demand he also grew as a social figure. He amiably squired ladies who found themselves lonely. He danced beautifully. As time passed he paid more and more attention to his clothes. No one would identify this elegant, well-mannered young man with the struggling art student who had embarked almost penniless from a grim London dock some eighteen months earlier. He was

careful never to presume upon the kindness of the aristocratic English colony in which he mingled. He took pains
to show a proper reticence. Unlike the majority of his
countrymen, he learnt Italian and French, so that he
became an asset in the international circles of Rome.
Under all this burned his intense passion to become the
great historical painter of the age. It was clear to many
of his colleagues that it was an ambition he could never
fulfil. His gift as an artist was mediocre. Incessant industry and hard study could not supply that touch of inspiration which transmutes the capable work into a thing of
genius. Happily, his sanguine temperament never realised
this fact.

His second Roman spring was even more intoxicating
than his first, and an event gave it an air of romance. One
warm evening in May, after an hour spent with the
Bunsens in Thorwaldsen's studio, to view the colossal
statues of Christ, St Peter and St Paul which had been
commissioned for a Copenhagen church, they all dined
in a little restaurant, *al fresco*, under its vine pergola.
The night was warm, and someone suggested a visit
to the puppet-show in a small theatre under the
Palazzo Fiano. They arrived in the dark. When the lamps
were turned up during the interval Severn found in the
row in front of him, with their mother, the two Miss
Walkers whom he had not seen since that happy day when
they had driven out to the Campagna with Bancroft,
Coolidge and himself.

He was delighted to see them again and learned that
they had been absent from Rome and at their villa in
Naples. He introduced them to the Bunsens. After the
puppet show, although it was midnight, they decided to
visit the Coliseum. It was a clear, starlit night with a full
moon that gave an awesome majesty to the vast ruin.
Severn had not met Mrs Walker before, and he found her

very sympathetic. For her part she felt an instant liking for this attractive young man with the beautiful head and the infectious laughter. On parting she invited him to call on her at her apartment in the Piazza Navona.

Throughout the next six weeks the Walker home became one of his favourite places of call. He would go round there in the evening after his work and spend agreeable hours, singing, playing the piano and sketching. It was a quiet, gentle atmosphere, and a pleasant change in its simplicity after the great palaces with their salons filled with the smart society of Rome.

One evening Mrs Walker announced that their lease of the apartment was up and in a week they would be returning to their little property in Naples. It was a villa on the slopes of Posilippo which belonged to her brother, Lord Elgin, and was their permanent home in Italy. Later Severn learned that Mrs Walker, greatly reduced in fortune and in poor health, lived in Italy, where she could maintain a better style with the loan of her brother's villa, than in England. Maria, the elder daughter, was twenty-three, a girl with a beautiful complexion, blue eyes and glorious tresses of blonde hair. Her sister, Julia, two years younger, was quieter in disposition. She was in love with a young Neapolitan of an excellent family that bitterly opposed the courtship on grounds of religion and finance.

When Severn expressed his dismay at the Walkers' impending departure for Naples, Mrs Walker asked why he did not come there for the summer months. She could find him cheap lodgings. There were endless subjects for his brush, the Revolution was over, and they could all make excursions together. So to Naples he went at the end of June. He was excited at the thought of seeing it again, but he was more excited at the thought of seeing Maria, for he was now in love with her.

They found him a big room high up on one of the hills of the city with a view across the glorious bay to Capri, which rose like a violet wraith in the shimmering heat of the summer. He worked in the mornings, rising at six to use the cool hours. After lunch and a siesta he went out to the Walkers' villa. It stood on the hillside above three terraces that led down to a small harbour in which they kept a boat. They lived most of the day on the top terrace shaded by a vine pergola. It was an earthly paradise, with the glittering blue bay before them. Across it rose the great cone of Vesuvius with its plume of smoke. How different it was from that rain-drenched scene he had known in those first days on Italian soil when he had landed with his sick friend!

Yet despite its beauty, the glorious days dreaming in the garden, the hours spent on their boat in the bay, the lovely starlit nights, the joyous companionship of the two sisters, it seemed that Naples held for him sinister omens. Towards the end of August he received a letter sent on from Rome. It was written by his friend Leigh Hunt who, with his family, had joined Lord Byron, now living in Pisa. It informed him how Shelley, after coming from his home in the bay of Lerici to call on him, had set forth again in his boat *Ariel* and had been caught in a storm and drowned. After ten harrowing days his body had been washed ashore and his remains cremated on the seashore at Viareggio, with Byron, Trelawny and himself present. When they examined Shelley's body they had found in his coat pocket a book doubled back as though the reader had hastily put it away. The book was Keats's last volume, *Lamia, Isabella, The Eve of St Agnes and Other Poems*, which Leigh Hunt had given Shelley in parting. The widow would send Shelley's ashes to be buried with his infant son in the Protestant Cemetery at Rome.

It was a glorious afternoon. Severn read the letter sitting on the terrace. The only letter he and Keats had received on landing here that November day two years ago had been a generous one from Shelley inviting him to come to Pisa. It was not the first gesture of its kind. Five years ago he and Keats had met this volatile spirit at Leigh Hunt's cottage. Keats admired him, but remained reserved towards Shelley's affability. Class-conscious, a liveryman's son, he was careful not to be patronised by the heir of a wealthy baronet. Both poets had made an early appearance in Leigh Hunt's paper *The Examiner*.

What happy days those had been, lit with their immeasurable hopes and ambitions. Poor Shelley! Severn knew the dark side of the picture. His own family had been horrified when they learned that his name had appeared in the Preface of *Adonais*. They protested against finding him praised by an atheist, a republican and free-liver, and begged him to cease all further acquaintance with a man of such vile reputation. It might jeopardise his scholarship. It was indeed true that Shelley had brought odium upon himself. He had been expelled from Oxford for atheism, he had deserted his child-wife Harriet, who had committed suicide after giving birth to his two children. He had committed adultery with Mary Wollstonecraft Godwin, the sixteen-year-old daughter of the sponging revolutionary Godwin. The guilty couple had fled abroad, accompanied by Claire Clairmont, who had pursued Byron and borne him a child. That poor little waif Allegra, placed by Byron in a convent at Bagnacavallo, had died only last April. Shelley, Mary, Claire Clairmont and her child, "the bastard" as Byron called his offspring, had travelled about Italy together. Shelley had married Mary Godwin, following the suicide of the deserted nineteen-year-old Harriet. He had come south

to Italy convinced that he was consumptive. A persecution mania had been acerbated by the scathing denuncia-
tion of the Lord Chancellor, who had denied him the
custody of his children by Harriet. He had been terrified
that the courts might deprive him of his adored little
William, his child by Mary, who, dead of fever, aged
three, in Rome, now lay near Keats in the Protestant
Cemetery. Notorious throughout England, irrational,
subject to hallucinations, the picture of Shelley was indeed
a dark one. And yet withal, what a generous, entrancing
spirit, fearless in attacking abuses, and possessed of such
charm that he drew to him a band of friends dazzled
equally by the man and the poet of genius. It did not seem
possible that so fierce a flame had been quenched in the
waters of the Mediterranean. In his noble elegy, Shelley
had called Keats "a pard-like spirit, beautiful and swift."
It was a fitting description of himself.

Thinking of Shelley and his noble lines to Keats,
Severn suddenly recalled the verses of the poem that was
the elegy of both these poets, dead so young:

> *He has outsoared the shadow of our night;*
> *Envy and calumny and hate and pain,*
> *And that unrest which men miscall delight,*
> *Can touch him not and torture not again.*

II

The holiday in Naples had been shattered by the news
of Shelley's death. Memories of the two poets seemed to
haunt the place, and Severn could not rid himself of an
obsession that menaced him. The shock had come at a
moment of tension. His growing passion for Maria Walker
had brought him to the verge of a declaration of love. A
person of a balanced nature, he had carefully debated the
problems that marriage would bring in its train. His

career was just opening. He was not sufficiently established to face without anxiety the financial burden of matrimony. Neither of them possessed any means. His own livelihood was precarious and based on the whims of transitory patrons endowed with all the inconstancy of the rich. Maria was twenty-three. He could well wait two or three years and get himself soundly established. It would be wise not to commit himself at present.

Severn became suddenly impatient to return to Rome, feeling a strong distaste for Naples. Not even the lovely villa and the hospitable family with whom he spent so much of his time checked his wish to depart. To the dismay of the Walkers, who had expected him to stay until they returned to Rome at the end of October, he announced his departure.

In the third week of September he returned to the Via San Isidoro. The English colony was beginning to come back from the mountains and the coast. Those who lived in England would arrive later, and not until October did their travelling coaches begin to line up in the Piazza di Spagna.

A month after his arrival in Rome Severn had another shock. At tea at Miss Fairleigh's he met John Cam Hobhouse, who had been with Byron during his visit to Rome in 1817. He had recently arrived and had made a call at Canova's studio. "As I was leaving, I asked after Canova, who was away. That same evening I heard he had died in Venice a few days earlier," he said.

The news stunned Severn. Canova had shown him much kindness. Every young student had found in him a friend. He had expended the whole of the Pope's pension in assisting them. The greatest figure in the world of art had gone.

CHAPTER IX

I

THE winter season opened with much gaiety. The King of Prussia and his two sons arrived in Rome. Parties were given for them by the Niebuhrs, the Bunsens, the Duchess of Devonshire and Prince Torlonia, to which Severn was asked. On many occasions he was the escort of Lady Westmorland, whose dresses and conversation always created a sensation. There was a *festa* with fireworks and St Peter's was illuminated. One day he went to Tivoli with Mr Bunsen, who was on duty to the King and had to supervise an entertainment at the Villa d'Este. All its terraced fountains played, and in the great salon above the gardens, overlooking the cypress avenue with its giant fountain, a luncheon for sixty was given in the King's honour. Throughout the previous day Severn and Bunsen had run around Rome hiring horses. Sixty-four were required for the eight royal carriages, thirty-two to start with and another thirty-two for a change halfway. Rome was almost exhausted on the departure of the royalties.

In the middle of December a long-lost friend arrived. Elton, more debonair than ever, had been absent in Vienna since the summer, visiting a cousin at the British Embassy. He was taken ill in Vienna, was in bed a month. "The old enemy," he said, tapping his chest. The music in Vienna had been wonderful—opera, ballet, concerts.

"I went to one I shall never forget! I heard a child of eleven play the piano—an absolute genius! The audience went mad. He's the son of a steward to Prince Esterhazy, who's been backing him. Franz Liszt. We shall hear of that boy one day."

He looked around the studio, tapping his Hessian boot with a gold-topped cane, then stopped in front of a portrait. "Who's this?" he asked. "Damn pretty girl!"

"It's Maria Walker. I did it in Naples this summer, where they've a villa."

"Then you had a pleasant summer?"

"Very, thank you," said Severn smiling.

"Well?" asked Elton, quizzingly.

"Well?" parried Severn.

"My dear fellow, you never lose your head, do you? Here you are, a young Adonis with all the women in Rome running after you and you never tumble—at least we see no signs of it. Even the gorgeous Lady Westmorland, a possessive gorgon if ever there was one, has no luck! How do you do it? With half your allure I can't keep free of entanglements."

"You forget I've my art," said Severn, guardedly.

Elton looked at him with an amused air.

"From what I see of art in this city, Venus provides more inspiration than Raphael. There's our friend Kirkup, for instance. I've just been round to find another new face sharing breakfast with him—the fourth face in a twelve-month, I swear!"

"When I find a face that I want to share breakfast with, I'll invite you to join," said Severn, laughing. "But at present I'm a poor struggling artist and matrimony would be a serious proposition."

"Matrimony! I don't suggest you should be as serious as that!"

"I'm a serious person, Elton."

"*Dio mio*, you are! How can you be so cruel to poor wenches!"

"There are plenty of public benefactors like yourself," retorted Severn, laughing.

Elton departed. Strange what a flame burned in him.

But for how long? Severn was shocked by his appearance. He was the same light-hearted fellow but in six months there had been a noticeable physical change. He had a transparent look, his eyes unnaturally bright. Severn knew the signs too well.

II

A few yards distance from the Caffé Greco in the Via dei Condotti stood the shop of Mr James Freeborn. He had long been established in Rome as a wine merchant who was consulted by the British Colony when making purchases of wine for shipment. He was a calm, sensible man, reliable in character and held in great esteem by his fellow countrymen. By reason of this standing, he had been asked by the British Government to undertake the rôle of British Consular agent, a task he most ably performed along with his business of wine merchant. At the back of his shop he had a sitting-room whose windows looked on to a sunny *patio* embellished with a grotto covered with green mosses and a little marble dolphin that spurted water. As was fitting for a man in the wine trade, Mr Freeborn took much pride in an old vine growing by one of the walls, whose branches were trained over the pergola. It gave a pleasant green shade in summer. Here Mr Freeborn was in the habit of inviting his friends and special customers to take a glass of Frascati or Orvieto wine. He was a congenial man who all his life had lived in the sunshine and radiated its warmth. In his office of Consul he fulfilled something of the rôle of confessor to those who brought their problems to him. He succeeded by infinite tact in keeping in with the Papal authorities whose tyrannical dispensation preserved Rome as the last stronghold of feudalism. Every day some problem was presented to him. He knew the devious ways, via monsignors, cardinals and their corruptible minions, by which some sort of rough justice could be obtained through the exercise of inexhaustible patience. It was a tribute to his skill and standing that his services were more often sought by Romans suffering from some injustice than by his fellow countrymen.

One morning towards the end of August a box had been delivered to his shop that was clearly not a consignment of wine. It was corded and sealed and had come by boat from Leghorn via Civitavecchia. A letter explained its surprising contents. A consular colleague, Mr Grant of Leghorn, informed him that the box contained the ashes of an Englishman, the late Mr Percy Bysshe Shelley of Casa Magna, Lerici, who had been drowned while sailing his boat from Leghorn to Lerici. The body had been washed up and cremated on the shore at Viareggio in the presence of Lord Byron, Mr Leigh Hunt and Mr Edward Trelawny, all friends of Shelley, who was a poet of some notoriety. It was the desire of the widow that Shelley's ashes should be deposited in the grave of his infant son William, who had died in Rome three years earlier and had been buried in the Protestant Cemetery there. Mr Trelawny would shortly come to Rome to attend to the disposition of the ashes.

Mr Freeborn was not in Rome when the box arrived. He was holidaying at Subiaco in the Sabine Hills. He had opened and read the letter while sitting in the garden of the Monastery of St Benedict, where the founder of the Benedictine Order had had his hermit's cell. Now enlarged with frescoed chapels and galleries, it clung like a martin's nest to the precipitous wall of a mountain nearly two thousand feet high, a venerated sanctuary since the twelfth century of the saint who, persecuted by a rival hermit, had migrated from there to found the Abbey of Monte Cassino.

About the middle of September Mr Freeborn returned to Rome. He found the box in his office. It was of plain chestnut, square and substantial, with nothing on it to indicate its contents. A little embarrassed by the contents of the box, he had it taken down into the wine cellar underneath his shop, a place not inappropriate, for tradition said that the alcoves occupied by the wine bins, being part of a catacomb, had once held the bones of early Christians. Soon the news of the box's contents leaked out and strange rumours began to be circulated about Rome. In this manner Mr Freeborn learned that he was the guardian of the ashes of a notorious atheist whose poetical works were banned from every respectable British home. October and November passed and there was no sign of Mr Trelawny. An appeal to Mr Grant in Leghorn brought no satisfactory reply.

One morning in the Via Condotti Mr Freeborn encountered Seymour Kirkup in the company of Joseph Severn. He was perturbed when Kirkup asked him whether it was true that he had a box containing the ashes of Shelley.

"What makes you ask me that question?" asked Freeborn with scarcely disguised annoyance.

"All Rome is talking about the box. Severn is interested in it. Last August he received a letter from Leigh Hunt in Pisa telling him Shelley's ashes were to be sent here for burial. I believe the heart is——"

Freeborn nervously cut him short.

"I think we had better go to my shop. It's not a thing to discuss in the street," he said.

Freeborn conducted Kirkup and Severn to his back sitting-room looking on to the *patio*. He opened a bottle and filled three glasses.

"Now, gentlemen," he said, after they had drunk, "what about this box? Something must be done soon. Last week a couple of the Prefect's minions called on me and asked whether I was harbouring an *heretical corpse*! I truthfully informed them that not an inch of any corpse was on my premises. The way they asked the question suggested that I was maturing my wines with human cadavers. They will come again, I fear. I cannot continue to hold this box if Mr Trelawny doesn't turn up soon. You say, Mr Severn, that you received a letter about the ashes?"

"Yes, my friend Mr Leigh Hunt, who is with Lord Byron in Pisa, and was present at the cremation, wrote to me some months ago saying Shelley's ashes would be sent to Rome for burial. Since then, until last week, when Kirkup told me of the rumours floating about, I have heard nothing further."

"Do you know this Mr Trelawny?"

"No. I believe he was a friend of Shelley's."

"You knew Shelley?" asked Freeborn.

"Yes. We had a mutual friend in Mr Leigh Hunt."

"Oh!"

"My dead friend John Keats and myself met Shelley at his house," explained Severn.

Freeborn was silent for a few moments.

"Mr Severn," he said, slowly, "it seems our melancholy fate to bury English poets in the Protestant Cemetery. My inclination is to return this box if Trelawny does not come soon. My position with the authorities may soon become very difficult. They have no delicacy in dealing with foreign heretics, as they deem us."

"I think it would be very fitting to bury Shelley in the Protestant Cemetery, if there is no obstacle," said Severn. "We are told Mrs Shelley desires it, but I'm sure it would be Shelley's wish also. He wrote an elegy on Keats, and in referring to the Cemetery he said: 'It might make one in love with death to think that one should be buried in so sweet a place.'"

"He wrote that?" asked Freeborn.

"Yes, in his Preface to *Adonais*," replied Severn.

L

"There seems every reason for placing his ashes there," said Kirkup. "Need we wait any longer for this Trelawny?"

"There's one obstacle. There's no Protestant clergyman in Rome at present," said Freeborn. "But, since you gentlemen agree, I shall act as soon as one comes."

Good fortune produced the necessary clergyman only a few days after Christmas. There came into Freeborn's shop a reverend gentleman, Richard Burgess, who required assistance in moving some manuscripts out of the Papal State. When the formalities had been attended to, Freeborn surprised the clergyman by asking if he would accompany him down to the cellar, as he had something he wished to show him. The clergyman assenting, Freeborn led the way down the steps, candle in hand. He halted in front of a square box.

"I have been waiting some time for a clergyman to come here. I want you to bury that box," he said.

"But what is in it?" asked Mr Burgess, surprised.

"Mr Shelley's ashes, sir. He was a poet, a notorious atheist, I believe, who was drowned off Viareggio last July. It is time he was buried, whatever his views."

"I would not agree that he was an atheist—he was young and foolish when at Oxford, and they treated a headstrong youth very harshly," said Mr Burgess.

"You knew him?"

"No; but I know of him. I regard him as one of our greatest poets. Indeed, we must bury him. I have a colleague travelling with me. I would like to consult him first."

"Certainly, Mr Burgess. The person who was to attend to all this, a Mr Trelawny, who cremated Shelley on the seashore, has not turned up. The news of these ashes here has leaked out and unpleasant rumours have begun to circulate."

"Then we must act quickly," said Mr Burgess. "One precaution we must take. The box must be put in a coffin, otherwise we might run into trouble with the authorities."

"I will attend to that at once, and make the other necessary arrangements," said Freeborn, greatly relieved.

III

In the first light of dawn, on January 21st, 1823, a small group of Englishmen set forth in two carriages and followed a hearse to the Protestant Cemetery. There were two clergymen, the Rev. Richard Burgess, the Rev. William Cook, General Cockburn, Sir Christopher Sykes, a Yorkshire baronet wintering in Rome, Mr Freeborn, and Severn and his three colleagues, Kirkup, Westmacott and Scoles. Of these only Severn had known the man whose ashes they were following, in a last reverent gesture to a fellow countryman. What a strange pattern of Fate was here, thought Severn. Only seventeen months apart in time, two young English poets, known to each other, and both to him, had died in Italy, and now took the same journey to sleep for ever in the cemetery of the English exiles in Rome.

Severn was acutely nervous. There had been a mishap. The old cemetery where Keats lay, in the shadow of the pyramid of Caius Cestius, had been abandoned. Although it was often desecrated, the authorities would not enclose it, as they asserted it would spoil the view, and that it belonged to the Roman people as a recreation meadow. They had wholly enclosed another portion of the meadow sloping down from the crumbling Aurelian Wall and set it apart for the burial of heretics. Here all new interments must take place. It was necessary, since father and son were to be together, for the grave of young William to be opened and his coffin transferred to the grave awaiting Shelley in the new cemetery. To their horror, on removing the child's headstone, they found in the opened grave the skeleton of a grown man. Further search was impossible, since they were closely watched by some Italians. So Shelley had to be buried without the company of his infant son.

The dawn broke cold and cloudy. Shelley's was the third grave in the new enclosure. It seemed inexpressibly lonely. A little distant, outside the new wall, lay John Keats.

CHAPTER X

IN February Severn moved into new quarters. He took a lease of an apartment with a large studio in the Via dei Meroniti. He had conceived the idea of starting a British Academy in Rome where the English artists could meet, study and exhibit their works. France had its Academy founded by Louis XIV, in the Villa Medici; the Austrians and the Spaniards also had their Academies. It seemed remiss for England to lag behind. Severn was elated when, after making a suggestion to Sir Thomas Lawrence, seconded by Lady Westmorland, who promised to enlist local support, the President of the Royal Academy sent him his warm approval and a personal gift of fifty pounds. Furthermore, he promised the venture a portrait of George IV to hang in the Academy's room. The Duchess of Devonshire made a donation and obtained one hundred pounds from the British Ambassador at Naples.

The new apartment in the Via dei Meroniti was part of a suppressed monastery. It had seven rooms on the top floor of a building just off the thronged Via del Tritone. There were three rooms on the north side, a necessary location during the heat of summer, and four on the south. The studio, the gallery and a bedroom and kitchen were on the north side. A long window opened on to a balcony that commanded a view of the gardens of the Quirinal, the Pope's residence, shut in from public view by high, bastioned walls. From this balcony Severn overlooked several acres of parterres and palms, fountains and a summer casino. A campanile with a clock crowned the Pope's private chapel. Severn could read the time from this baroque clock. Gibson, Kirkup and Westmacott, whom he had taken to view the place, were most enthusiastic. So the Academy of Rome was launched. Lady Westmorland supplied several pieces of furniture and Severn found a man and his wife to take charge of the premises. At the end of March he was installed. Her ladyship was his first caller. She was most complimentary about his new quarters, viewing the disposal of her three *cinquecento* chairs, Florentine chest and Genoese velvet curtains with approval. Already the studio began to be attractive.

II

Spring descended on Rome early that year and the weather grew suddenly warm. There were excursions to the Campagna, and Severn again saw much of Maria Walker. The family were back in their apartment, and he persuaded Maria to sit for him in the rôle of Miranda in a picture called "Ferdinand and Miranda." Elton watched the affair with amusement. One day Kirkup annoyed Severn with a pointed remark. "You'll never take the jump as long as Lady Westmorland's on the scene," he commented.

"My life is in no way controlled by her," retorted Severn.

He knew, however, there was much truth in Kirkup's remark. Lady Westmorland was possessive. She made her plans, including him without gaining his consent previously. He made a struggle for independence, but she was too domineering. She believed that the whole of Rome was created for her amusement. Anyone not willing to accept this conception was classed as an enemy. She fought with Lady Compton, a sturdy little Scotswoman who was not willing to be dominated. She had quarrelled with the Duchess of Devonshire because that lady had unwittingly planned a ball for the same evening as Lady Westmorland's and had declined to postpone it. For a month she snubbed the French Ambassador, the Duc de Laval-Montmorency, because he had gone to the Duchess's ball, as he had previously accepted, instead of coming to hers.

Having discovered that Severn was a good pianist, she decided that he should play duets with her whenever the whim took her. Once when she had sent her carriage for him for this purpose she was outraged because he declined to leave his easel. The next morning she arrived at the studio and gave him a lecture in good manners, having none herself when in a temper. She was outrageously unpunctual and often embarrassed him, when escorting her, by arriving at a dinner party an hour late. Sometimes she seemed to have forgotten the guests she had invited for lunch or dinner and descended to the salon, where they had waited for three-quarters of an hour, without any consciousness of being late. Yet such were her beauty and vitality, the brilliance of her talk, and the melting graciousness she could assume at will, that very few declined to be managed by her.

Severn was deeply indebted to Lady Westmorland. She had taken him into Society; she was ruthless in procuring commissions for him from her titled and wealthy friends. He could never forget her help at a time when he was greatly perturbed over the loss in transit of his Academy picture. But for her solicitations, her letters to Sir Thomas Lawrence, he might never have gained the Travelling Scholarship or found the means to remain in Rome.

She treated his affair with Maria Walker with amusement and was deft in disparagement. "A pretty girl—but insipid. I can never get an intelligent remark out of her. Tell me, Mr Severn, what do you talk about when you are with her?" she asked him one day, calling at his studio, Maria having just departed. "Or do you just sit in silence and worship—'quiet as a nun, breathless with adoration' as Mr Wordsworth puts it?" She laughed merrily at his embarrassment.

"I think, ma'am, you never see Maria at her best. You terrify her," said Severn.

"I terrify her? My dear Mr Severn, no one could call me terrifying! Now, if I were the Duchess of Devonshire, the Dragon, perhaps—or Lady Compton, who rides over one like a mail coach, yes!"

Despite Lady Westmorland, he saw much of Maria that spring. Elton lent them a pair of horses, and they took rides over the Campagna. They met and danced at the innumerable parties given in Rome. And yet somehow the urge to make a proposal grew less. Lady Westmorland had found the flaw in his lovely Galatea. Maria was insipid.

He was expecting her one morning to give him another sitting when there was a peremptory rap on his studio door. When he opened it, he found a swarthy man of about thirty standing on the threshold. He was dressed in a vivid blue shirt and white nankeen trousers. A red kerchief was wound round his tawny throat. His skin had a mahogany tan and his black curly hair and the moustache over the full red lips gave him the air of a gipsy. Most noticeable of all were his grey falcon eyes which denoted a swift, intractable temper. But he smiled now with flashing teeth as he spoke.

"Joseph Severn? I'm Edward Trelawny," he said, stepping into the studio without any invitation. "You've got a nice eagle's nest here," he added, looking around him. "Leigh Hunt told me a good bit about you and Keats."

From that moment, for the whole of the following week, Severn felt dominated by this extraordinary man. His appearance was as astonishing as his conversation. Most people found him terrifying. "A brigand," said Lady Westmorland. "A colossus," said Kirkup. "Sinister," said Elton. "A bit of a liar, I feel," observed Catherwood. Mr Freeborn expressed no opinion, but he watched him warily. Trelawny had come at last to deal with the business of Shelley's grave. He at once expressed disapproval. "We can't have the ashes of our noble Shelley mixed up with half a dozen nondescripts," he said, on viewing the grave in the lower part of the cemetery.

Freeborn looked at him coldly. "Mr Trelawny, I do my best for those who are entrusted to me for burial."

"I mean no offence, but we shall never look on a man like Shelley again," replied Trelawny. "Mrs Shelley has authorised me to make arrangements satisfactory to her. I propose moving Shelley's ashes up there by the Aurelian Wall."

He pointed to a recess made by a fortification tower in the old wall. It was at the top of the sloping ground.

"You will, of course, do as you wish. The matter is out of my hands," said Freeborn, coolly.

Trelawny lost no time. He bought the recess with space for two graves, called in a mason to make two vaults, planted a row of cypresses, and ordered a memorial stone on which he engraved *Cor Cordium*, adding three lines from *The Tempest*, much loved by Shelley:

> *Nothing of him that doth fade,*
> *But doth suffer a sea change*
> *Into something rich and strange.*

To everyone's surprise, though Trelawny dressed like a common sailor and lived in an inn of the cheapest kind, he produced the money for these arrangements. When asked what the second grave was for, he said, "Myself. Shelley is the greatest man I've ever known. One day I shall be brought here to lie by him. All that will be necessary will be to raise the stone and roll me in."

"Melodramatic," commented Kirkup on hearing this.

"I don't think so," answered Severn. "The fellow really has a tremendous admiration for Shelley."

One night just before his departure, at a gathering in Severn's studio that he must have felt congenial, he began to talk freely. He held them spellbound with stories of his adventures as a cadet in the cockpit of H.M.S. *Colossus*, the old seventy-four gunner badly mauled at Trafalgar; of fighting pirates off Goa in the Indian seas; of deserting his ship; of becoming a boy captain of a privateer; of a strange marriage to a young Arab wife, daughter of an island sheikh, of her death by poison designed for himself, of her cremation on the seashore; of his killing his mutinous French boatswain, Malay fashion—the *creese* driven under the shoulder through the back into the heart —here Trelawny stood up to give an explanatory illustration of the killing—of throwing his body to the sharks; of his adoption of a little Malay slave girl and of her suicide on his departure for England; all this before he was twenty. He went on and narrated the story of his marriage in England, his discovery of his wife's lover, followed by divorce proceedings, his meeting with Shelley and Byron at Pisa, and, lastly, a tremendous episode that held them spellbound, his description of the cremation of Shelley's body last August on the seashore at Viareggio.

"The heart wouldn't burn, I scorched my hand snatching it out of the furnace—for nothing," said Trelawny. "Look!"

He held out a strong brown hand with the flesh scarred by burning. A silence fell on the company.

"For nothing, how?" asked Catherwood, after a pause.

"I thought Mary Shelley might like his heart, but she wouldn't have it," said Trelawny quietly.

"Then it is here, in his grave?" asked Elton.

"No."

"No?" repeated Severn.

"Leigh Hunt begged so hard for it, I gave it to him."

A cold tremor passed over the company. For an hour they had been spellbound by his astonishing story. How much was true, how much the creation of a gifted narrator? The finale with its story of Shelley's heart closed the recital on a macabre note.

"And what is your next adventure?" asked Elton.

There was a shade of derision in the question that did not pass unnoticed by Trelawny.

"If you have that much interest in my welfare, I will tell you," said Trelawny, turning his grey eyes coldly on Elton. "I've just bought two cavalry horses from an Austrian colonel here and engaged a Negro groom to look after them. On Friday I shall start off for Florence, riding in the cool of the morning and sleeping Arab fashion wherever I find myself. If there is any healthier or pleasanter way of life than this, I have never enjoyed it." He surveyed his elegantly dressed questioner from head to foot. "But you would not appreciate it," he added with a derisive smile. "Afterwards I shall go to Genoa to see Byron. He may be leading an expedition to Greece, to liberate it from the Turks. I hear he would like me to join him. It might be a great adventure."

Trelawny left early one May morning. His visit had stimulated all the gossips of Rome. A short while before his departure Severn wrote to his old friend Charles Armitage Brown, who had come out from England and settled in Florence: "There is a mad chap come here whose name is Trelawny. I do not know what to make of him." That summed up the impression he had created in Rome—impressive, mysterious, sinister. But on one thing they all agreed. He had procured a splendid site for Shelley's resting-place and performed his mission with the greatest taste.

III

In June, having received a commission to make a copy of Raphael's *Madonna della Sedia* in the Pitti Gallery, again owing to Lady Westmorland's interest, Severn departed for Florence. It gave him an opportunity of visiting his old friend Brown. What memories their association evoked! It was he who had gone off with Keats on that fatal walking tour in Scotland. Brown had built with a friend a white Regency house below Hampstead Heath called Wentworth Place. It was in this house that Keats had first met Fanny Brawne, aged eighteen. It was to Wentworth Place he had rushed from the death of his brother Tom to break the news to Brown; in its garden he had heard the nightingale sing; there he had lived the greatest year of his life, 1819, when his genius had its miraculous flowering. In one half of that house, while he was lodging with Brown, the Brawnes, mother and daughter, had come as tenants. Its walls had seen the play of passion between the ill-starred lovers:

> *He knew whose gentle hand was at the latch*
> *Before the door had given her to his eyes;*
> *And from her chamber-window he would catch*
> *Her beauty farther than the falcon spies;*

Thus Keats had written in reminiscence of that period. Never had there been such a spring in English literature, with the odes *To a Nightingale*, *On a Grecian Urn*, *To Autumn*, all born of it.

It was in one room of Brown's house, on a night of February, 1820, that Keats had read his death-warrant in the blood coughed on to a bedsheet. He lay sick there.

It was there he had taken Severn to meet the Brawnes, and finally it was in the Brawnes's half of that square white house that Fanny and her mother had nursed the poet now conscious of his imminent doom. From that house he had set forth for Italy; there he had made his farewell to Fanny. He had ceased, as he put it, "to be a citizen of this world." It had been hoped that Brown would take him to Italy, but he was away. Someone mentioned Severn, the young artist who might be able to maintain himself in Rome. And so into the breach he had stepped.

To be with Brown was to relive those sad vivid Hampstead days. It was a Brown not greatly changed, portly, bald, a dilettante of letters with a small income, a happy-go-lucky *bon viveur*, generous in spirit, nearing forty. An affair with his Irish maidservant had produced a boy now living with him in Florence.

For Severn, wrapped in warm companionship in the lively Florentine atmosphere, there was a flavour of home, long missed. He worked desperately hard in the next three months, with promise of a trip to Venice. Florence was full of the English, settled there or coming and going. Brown had a floor of a palazzo overlooking the Ponte Vecchio. Near him still lived the ex-wife of Bonnie Prince Charlie, the elderly but vivacious Countess of Albany, who, having dwelt there for many years with her lover Alfieri, now cohabited with his successor, Fabre, the French portrait painter. At her thronged receptions she sat in a chair blazoned with the arms of the Royal Stuarts, demanding homage as a rightful Queen of England. For the second time Severn glimpsed her one evening at an opera composed by Lord Burghersh, the resident British Minister to the Grand Duchy of Tuscany.

The Bonapartes had been driven out of Florence after usurping the Grand Ducal throne, but with the passing of

Elise, Napoleon's sister, a Hapsburg was restored who laboured to revive the splendours of the Medici Court. An era of kindly gaiety was inaugurated, having its centre in the vast Palazzo Pitti.

England was represented by a young man of singular gifts. Severn regarded with particular interest young Lord Burghersh, the stepson of Lady Westmorland. He was a figure of romance. Thirty-nine years of age, handsome, married to Lady Priscilla Wellesley, he had served with distinction in Sicily and Egypt, and with the Iron Duke at Vimiero and Talavera in Portugal and Spain. He had also served with the allied armies under Prince Schwarzenberg in Germany and later had taken part in the capture of Paris. To his distinction as a soldier he added that of a diplomat. After service in Paris, he had been appointed at the end of 1814 Extra Envoy and Minister Plenipotentiary at Florence, and had been also employed in the allied negotiations following Waterloo and Murat's execution which had resulted in the restoration of the Bourbons to Naples.

This record alone would have made him a distinguished figure. He had also a background of romance, for he was the son of the tenth Earl of Westmorland, who, as a young man, had fled to Gretna Green with Sarah, the daughter of the rich banker, Robert Child, who had passed over their son and left his great fortune and Osterley Park with all its treasures to the boy's sister. Young Burghersh had not allowed this rebuff of Fate to mitigate his energy. Not only as a soldier and diplomat had he won distinction, but in another field he had gained considerable reputation as a musician. He had studied under Zeidler, Platoni and Bianchi. Had he wished, he might have won acclaim as a violinist. Lord Burghersh had written a book of memoirs covering his campaigns with Wellington and Schwarzenberg, and had also written three operas, *Bajazet*, *Feda* and *Il Torneo*, all produced at Florence. He had just returned from London, where he had conceived and carried into execution the founding of the Royal Academy of Music. Such was the singular man to whom Lady Westmorland gave Severn a letter of introduction.

"I hope, Mr Severn, you can be present at the first night of my new opera, *The Rape of Proserpine*, next Friday? May I send you tickets?" he asked in the course of a very gracious reception.

Severn expressed his pleasure and accepted. He was invited to stay to dinner, and soon established the pleasantest relations with young Lady Burghersh, who had great talent as a portrait artist. It was a family dinner with the children present, including the little son and heir, George Fane. A beautiful portrait of mother and son, recently painted by Sir Thomas Lawrence, hung in the dining-room, and in the salon overlooking the Arno Severn admired a bust of his hostess, the work of Bartolozzi. It was an admirable representation of a woman of singular beauty and sweetness.

Severn came away from the palazzo enchanted with the Burghershes. At an early opportunity he was to be presented by the Minister to the Grand Duke, who, Burghersh assured him, would give him every facility for his work in the palace galleries.

"I never knew such a fellow!" commented Brown on his return. "Everything falls into your lap. What a thing it is to be handsome and endowed with such devastating charm! No one takes any notice of me. Why should they, with a body and brain like mine?"

"Nonsense. Didn't Lord Byron ask you to contribute to his *Review*?" retorted Severn.

"Leigh Hunt brought that about. The truth is, my dear fellow, I am a dilettante, ruined, as so many, by a barely adequate private income. I foresee some more luck for you. Someone's arrived whom you've got to paint."

"Who?"

"The beautiful Lady Blessington. She's here with her husband and her lover, Count D'Orsay. She's full of Lord Byron, whom she's seen at Genoa. She tells me he's committed himself to a crusade for the Greeks. He's commissioned Captain Roberts to find him a boat. The last boats that Roberts procured were the *Ariel*, which drowned Shelley, and the *Bolivar*, Byron's boat in which Trelawny went off with Shelley's ashes after the cremation. I don't consider the signs propitious!"

"I shan't have much chance with Lady Blessington," said Severn. "Portraits are not my line. Also, a beauty who's been painted by Lawrence and D'Orsay wouldn't waste time on me. All London raves over Lawrence's study."

"You'll see D'Orsay at the Opera on Friday—quite incredible! He held up the carriages in the Via Tornabuoni to-day. Lavender trousers, high-heeled shoes of red suède, a waistcoat of sequins and a bottle-green coat with tails flapping on his calves. The dandy of dandies—damn good-looking, I must say. The entourage, with Lord Blessington bringing up the rear, descended on Florence last Monday. It numbered eight coaches and thirty lackeys, including Napoleon's cook, whom she picked up in Paris. The 'Blessington Circus,' as it's called, carries other baggage in the form of a nice little scandal that's blowing around."

"Florence, it seems to me, has as many scandals blowing around as it has villas," commented Severn.

"This is a special one, my dear fellow. It seems that Blessington's legitimate boy, the heir, died a couple of months ago. It so shook the amiable Earl that he made a new Will in Genoa. He has two bastards, a boy and a girl, who can't inherit. So his legitimate daughter, Harriet, only twelve, mark you, has been willed to D'Orsay, of all people. She must marry him or lose her inheritance. And D'Orsay is the property of Lady Blessington, Harriet's stepmother! There's a plot worthy of Euripides for you!"

"Wherever do you get all this?" asked Severn.

"At lunch at Princess Torrigiani's to-day I met a lady who has just come from Genoa. They began to talk about D'Orsay and Blessington. Miss Fairleigh has a——"

"Who?" asked Severn.

"Miss Fairleigh."

"A tall, middle-aged woman with a long neck and drooping eyelids?"

"That describes her pretty well. Miss Fairleigh has a friend who's in the British Consul's office at Genoa, and he had something to do with the Will."

"Consuls' clerks shouldn't talk!" said Severn.

"No, but they do. Anyhow, Florence is buzzing with the story."

"The busiest buzzer of all is Miss Fairleigh. *Dio mio!* You didn't by any chance get on to the subject of Nelson?" asked Severn.

"No. Why?"

"One of the bees buzzing in her bonnet concerns Nelson. Have you seen Lady Blessington yet?"

"No; but everyone tells me she is ravishing and witty— Irish, about thirty. She was married at fifteen to an Army captain, says Miss Fairleigh, who knew the Farmer family into which she married."

"Who doesn't Miss Fairleigh know, I wonder!" commented Severn. "But go on."

"He was a sadistic brute and after three months she refused to stay with him. Mrs Farmer returned home for three years. Then her father, a drunken roysterer, shot a

M

lad and was tried for murder and acquitted. But he was ruined. To get away from it all, she formed an intimacy with a Captain Jenkins. She lived with him for five years. He treated her kindly, they say. Then one day a friend, Lord Mountjoy, came on a visit. His story's very odd, according to Miss Fairleigh. He was thirty, rich, mad about theatricals. He fell in love with a brother officer's wife, a Mrs Browne. Her husband went off on foreign service and left Mrs Browne in Mountjoy's care. By him she had two children. Major Browne disappeared completely and was presumed dead. Now listen to this! I can't believe Miss Fairleigh invented it. Mountjoy felt he should marry Mrs Browne, in case of future events. He did so. Major Browne thereupon turned up! For a certain sum he consented to disappear. Mountjoy, a little worried, had another wedding. Soon after that the news of Browne's death, undeniable this time, reached them. So Mrs Browne, now really a widow, married Mountjoy for a third time! But it didn't legitimise his children by her, the daughter and son. After the third marriage the lady had another daughter and son, and then died. Mountjoy gave her a gorgeous funeral. Two years later he visited his friend, Captain Jenkins, then living with Mrs Farmer, whom Mountjoy had remembered for her loveliness. The visits were repeated. Mountjoy inherited the earldom of Blessington and thought Mrs Farmer would make a beautiful companion. He bought her from Jenkins for ten thousand pounds and installed her in a London suburb, but he behaved correctly. Unhappily, the lady again had an impediment—a husband still living, Captain Farmer. Later he obligingly fell from the window of a debtor's prison and was killed. So all ended happily and Sally, via Farmer, Jenkins and Blessington, became a real Countess. Then a year ago Count D'Orsay moved in, with the Earl's assent. It is a singular set-up. Miss Fairleigh, who knows the Countess, says her disposition is as sweet as her face is beautiful."

"A bon-bon from a cat!" exclaimed Severn. "Naturally, I'm agog to see her."

"Perhaps Miss Fairleigh will arrange it, but I hear their visit is to be short. They are bound for Rome and Naples."

In the next few weeks Severn saw Lady Blessington four times. She was undoubtedly beautiful, and a brilliant conversationalist. She was full of reminiscences of Lord Byron, whom she had seen in Genoa making his plans for the Greek expedition. She had recorded their conversations in her diary. "One day they might be considered history: he's a man of destiny most surely," she said to Severn and Brown.

D'Orsay, a youth of twenty-two, proved no fool, despite the trappings of the dandy. Severn was impressed by a portfolio of portraits from his pencil that Lady Blessington persuaded him to show. Lord Blessington was an amiable nonentity.

Rich, picturesque, popular, the Blessington circus was widely entertained, but one palazzo never received them. Lady Burghersh, virtuous mother of a young family, had strict views on social propriety. It was soon noted in the small English circle that the one palazzo where the visiting English expected to receive official hospitality was closed to the Blessingtons. One night at the opera Lord Burghersh coldly acknowledged D'Orsay's salute and the dandy's handsome face flushed with annoyance. The Grand Duke received them. Florence was split into pro- and anti-Blessington camps. Brown became devoted to them, but then he, too, was the father of an illegitimate child who went everywhere with him. Severn, with some anxiety, received both Lady Burghersh and Count D'Orsay in the

studio that had been lent to him, praying they would not
meet. Severn's anxiety filled Walter Savage Landor with
mirth. He threatened to bring Lady Burghersh and Lady
Blessington together in Severn's studio.

"She's a stiff-neck," said Landor of the Minister's wife.
"She must know all about her Uncle Wellington's run-
about with Harriette Wilson, so why be down on poor
Sally Blessington? Of the two sinners, I think I should
prefer the Irish one to the Iron one. When you've had as
much petticoat trouble as I've had, my dear Severn,
you'll know human nature just can't be regulated."

The threat was never fulfilled, for oddly enough Landor
never met the Blessingtons. He had avoided meeting the
Shelleys in Pisa owing to the scandal attached to them.
He thought it prudent not to meet the Blessingtons. At
that moment he was in the bad graces of the Grand
Duke, who, after a gross breach of hospitality, had
ordered him to leave the Duchy. Landor announced that
as the authorities disliked his residence he would reside
there permanently. The good-natured Grand Duke
ignored the retort. Landor prudently shut himself up in
the Palazzo Medici, where he lived turbulently with a
peevish wife, four undisciplined children and a horde of
yapping dogs. He had had scenes not only with the Grand
Duke and the Burghershes, but with almost everyone in
Florence, from the Podestà down to the chestnut-vendors.
Most people ran from him; a few adored him. Severn
belonged to the latter.

IV

The Blessingtons departed at the end of June. The
ripples they had made in the Florentine scene faded out.
Burghersh's opera was produced with much success, even
allowing for the natural enthusiasm that greeted the work
of an official of his distinction and charm. Severn worked

prodigiously, producing nineteen paintings in all. While he was in Florence he was distressed by news of the destruction of St Paul's Outside the Walls, the magnificent basilica just beyond the Protestant Cemetery and near the site of St Paul's martyrdom. It had been founded by the Emperor Constantine and through the centuries had grown into one of the glories of Christian Rome. Some drunken masons and plumbers, working on the roof, had quarrelled. One of the plumbers threw his pan of burning charcoal at a mason. In a few hours the great roof had been consumed, the ninth-century mosaics and magnificent columns calcined. Mrs Bunsen, who had sent Severn the news, said the fire had not been detected until two in the morning, when a monk in the adjoining monastery saw flames and gave the alarm. Long before the fire brigades could reach the basilica, the wooden roof, a thousand years old and dry in the heat of July, had collapsed. This loss was kept from the knowledge of the dying Pope.

After an excursion to Venice with Brown in August, Severn returned to Rome. He found that Lady Westmorland was back, more exigent than ever.

In November a new Pope, Leo XII, having been elected, Rome burst into a spate of festivities. Lady Compton, the Duc de Laval, Prince Doria and the Duchess of Devonshire gave balls. Provoked, Lady Westmorland decided to give one that should make history. She imported a Hungarian orchestra, lit the suite of salons with a thousand candles and invited eight hundred guests. She entered the ballroom half an hour late dressed as Cleopatra, wearing a magnificent emerald collar and a diamond asp fastened to her half-exposed breast. It was the most daring and dazzling costume Rome had seen for a century and was talked of for a week. A negro page with gilded hair carried her ostrich fan. At

4 a.m. half a ton of rose leaves fluttered down from the ceiling for a final *danse parfumée* and the guests revolved through a pink snowfall. When they departed their carriages drove out of the courtyard between two long avenues of footmen holding torches.

It was conceded that Lady Westmorland had surpassed all competitors. Even Prince Torlonia felt she had set a standard he could not live up to. Before retiring to bed at 8 a.m. she wrote a note to Bunsen, who had not accepted her invitation, saying she would bring his insulting behaviour to the notice of his master, the King of Prussia. The next day she forbade Severn to go to any parties at the Palazzo Caffarelli. He refused to observe this ban, and for a week she sent him to Coventry. Then one morning she suddenly appeared with Prince Leopold of Saxe-Coburg, whose wife Charlotte had died in childbirth at Claremont six years earlier. She persuaded him to buy Severn's *Peasant Girl Praying to the Madonna*. Thus Severn was handsomely forgiven. No further word was said about his friendship with the Bunsens.

The week before Christmas Elton appeared at the studio in a state of ecstasy. A new beauty had appeared on the scene and had convulsed young Rome.

"My dear Severn, you never saw anything so ravishing, so angelic in your life! I could not believe my eyes! I'd heard about her for a fortnight. Young Ruspoli was inarticulate when he tried to describe her—but you know these Roman Lotharios. Then I heard Laval-Montmorency was running around with his mouth watering— silly old dog! Catherwood's raving, and Gibson says she is Galatea come to life again and is begging her aunt to let her pose for him, which she firmly refuses. You must see her! She stopped the ball at Torlonia's last night and there was almost a fight among the effervescing youths to take her in to supper. She——"

Severn put down his palette and turned from the easel.

"My dear intoxicated friend, will you sit down, recover your calm and try to be articulate?" he asked. "Who is this Italian Galatea? Every season produces a new wonder."

"She's not Italian. She's English. Miss Bathurst—Rosa Bathurst. She's only sixteen. She's here with her aunt and uncle. Quite a tragic story. Her father was in the Diplomatic Service. Just after her birth he was sent with despatches through Prussia, then occupied by Napoleon's troops. He suddenly disappeared and has never been heard of since. Not a sign of his body—murdered by the French for the despatches, it is believed. Miss Bathurst feels she has a mission to discover his fate one day. She's something of an heiress, I believe, but the aunt's very vigilant. She needs to be. If you could see her! It's sheer heaven to watch her. Never, never, have I seen anything so lovely; and that's not only my opinion, it's everybody's!"

"And just what is Miss Bathurst like?" asked Severn. "Blonde or brunette?"

"A beautiful figure, tall, slender, lovely bosom, dazzling complexion—a rose just opening, dark melting eyes, hair like an aureole, a perfect throat, wonderful grace in every movement, just shy enough to keep one nervous, and a voice of pure music."

"I congratulate you. If I could paint like that, Raphael would have a rival," commented Severn.

"But Severn, I am very serious!"

"You always are, till you begin again."

"When you see her you will realise words can't describe her," avowed Elton.

"Miss Bathurst has a very serious rival."

"Who?"

"The famous Madame Récamier, who is in Rome," answered Severn.

"She must be an old woman! I've heard my father rave about her. When he was in Paris in 1814, on Wellington's staff, he said the Duke met her at Madame de Staël's and lost his head. He began scribbling notes to her and she had to snub him in the end."

"1814 is not so very long ago. I am assured that she's still a beauty. I shall be able to judge in a few hours. The Duchess of Devonshire's taking me to call."

"Well, you can have Madame Récamier. I'm for Miss Bathurst," said Elton eagerly, rising to leave.

Severn smiled at the elegant young man, immaculate as ever in shining Hessian boots, light green breeches and a heliotrope coat with wide lapels faced with beige silk.

"And just what are you doing to entice the maiden?" he asked.

Elton tapped his leg with his gold-topped cane. "It's fortunate for me that her passion's riding. I hear she's a superb horsewoman. To-morrow we are riding in the Villa Borghese. After that the Campagna. Somehow I must shake off Laval and Uncle Bathurst. Auntie's already in hand."

He laughed gaily, cried "*Arrivederci*" at the door and ran down the steps to the street.

Madame Récamier at forty-six was still a beautiful woman, though no longer the sylph who had infatuated Prince Augustus of Prussia to the point of folly. She had conferred immortality on David, who painted her reclining on a couch, and on Gérard, who painted her sitting on a chair. Yet she was still the alluring woman who had dared to rebuff Napoleon, who sent her into exile. Her salon drew the intellect of Paris. Chateaubriand loved her with a passion intense if not exclusive. Rumour said that her presence in Rome was due to a rift in their relationship. The rift apart, she had many reasons for coming to

Rome. During a visit to London at the opening of the century she had conquered it. She had made a sensational appearance in the Duchess of Devonshire's box at Covent Garden along with the Prince of Wales, the exiled Duc d'Orleans and the Duc de Montpensier. The crowd surrounding her carriage almost swept her off her feet. The woman of whom Lamartine had said, "Her angelic face can bear no other name; one look suffices to bind your heart forever," could even now cast a spell. Rome on her coming had paid tribute to her renown and beauty.

When the Duchess of Devonshire and Severn arrived at Madame Récamier's apartment in the Via Babuino her salon was thronged. The Duc de Laval-Montmorency was there, an old friend who had placed at her disposal his servants, carriages and horses. Severn saw the familiar face of the old Abbé Canova, the dead sculptor's brother. Despite Napoleon's past enmity, a number of the Bonaparte clan, Prince Canino, Prince Jerome and ex-Queen Hortense, were present. Severn was amused to observe how here, as elsewhere, the Duc de Laval-Montmorency, as Ambassador of Louis XVIII, and the other Bourbon legitimists, carefully kept apart from the Bonapartes.

Madame Récamier greeted the Duchess of Devonshire and smiled graciously at Severn, adding a few appropriate words of welcome. Her voice was low and beautiful. In every movement there was grace. At once Severn was struck with the sweetness of her face. It shone with unaffected kindness. Lady Westmorland, arriving towards the end of the reception, swiftly took the centre of the floor, appropriated the Duc de Laval-Montmorency, commanded Severn to sit by her and remarked to the Duchess of Devonshire: "You look very tired, dear Duchess. You must not worry over the poor Cardinal. All will be well."

It was a doubly tactless remark. All Rome knew that the

Duchess adored Consalvi, and his desperate illness darkened her days. But she smiled at Lady Westmorland and said amiably, "Thank you. I hope so." A few minutes later she asked Severn to escort her to her carriage.

"Well, what do you think of Madame Récamier?" the Duchess asked, as they drove away.

"She justifies David's masterpiece," he replied.

"The odd thing is that neither she nor David really like it! It is still in his studio, she tells me. She is very delicate. I was amused to see Canino there. He adored her and infuriated Napoleon by paying court to her. How silly of Napoleon! How could anyone not love Julie Récamier!"

She set Severn down in the Via del Tritone. Lady Westmorland had been tactlessly right about the Duchess of Devonshire. He noticed how tired and drawn she appeared.

v

The season was the gayest Rome had ever known. Prince August of Prussia arrived in the City, still uncured of an old passion. It was said he travelled with Gérard's portrait of the woman who had rebuffed him so cruelly. His coming gave the Bunsens many tasks. At the end of January Cardinal Consalvi died. He had been deposed from power on the death of Pius VII. His long reign in high office had created many enemies, but he was loved by a wide circle for his generosity, piety and learning. The blow was heavy on the Duchess of Devonshire. Rome laughed at her passion, though aware that it was harmless. The Cardinal was hurried away into oblivion. The pace of Rome was too swift to pause for the obsequies of a Prince of the Church. All thoughts were on the forthcoming balls that would mount in numbers and splendour until Carnival was over.

Maria Walker was back in Rome with her mother and sister. Again Severn frequented their apartment and courted Maria in a desultory fashion. It was through her and not through Elton, now consumed by despairing passion, that Severn met Rosa Bathurst. Madame Apponyi held a fête at the Austrian Embassy. For the entertainment of her guests she had a French comedy and a charade. Madame Récamier's niece, Mademoiselle Cyvort, acted the part of a soubrette in the comedy with the greatest success. She was pretty and her French diction was music. The charade was called *Délire*. The tableau of the first syllable *Dé* showed a set of players at dice, after a picture by Veronese. The principal player's wife and children made a group looking on, represented by the beautiful Princess Razumoffsky and the two Apponyi children. The second tableau was *Lyre*. In it seemed to have been gathered the most beautiful young women in Rome. Sappho playing the lyre was represented by Lady Frances Leveson-Gower. She looked like a Parian marble finely chiselled by Praxiteles. About her were four nymphs, Maria Walker, Mlle Pallavacini, Signorina Bischi, the current belle of the Italian girls, and a fourth of such devastating beauty that she drew all eyes.

"Rosa Bathurst," whispered Kirkup in Severn's ear.

She explained and justified Elton's lyricism in describing her. She was a lovely English rose in the first bloom of adolescence. Features and colouring were flawlessly blended. The audience, hypnotised by the exquisite group of virginal beauty, looked on the English girl wondering if it were possible that she belonged to life and was not the emanation of an artist's dream. Severn thought that never in human shape had he seen such perfect beauty. Maria, lovely as she was, scarcely existed at her side.

The closing tableau, representing *Délire*, revealed

King Saul with Jonathan and Michal, tawny and fair, one the son of Prince Doria-Pamphili. Presently a blond boy, with golden curls that Apollo would have coveted, came in with a harp and sang to the King in a beautiful tenor voice. He was the son of the Bavarian Minister. But what he sang seemed oddly incongruous, for it came from Rossini's opera *La Donna del Lago*, a four-year-old success.

Severn went to the fête with the Bunsens. Just in front of him sat Madame Récamier with the Duchess of Devonshire and Laval. Lady Westmorland absented herself, annoyed that her suggestion that the charade be from Scott's *Quentin Durward*, one of the Waverley novels taking the world by storm, was ignored. "Why all this *réclame* for the French, who have devastated Europe?" she protested.

The next time Severn saw the lovely Miss Bathurst was at a splendid ball Prince Torlonia gave in Carnival week. His English horses had again triumphed in the Corso. All that great wealth could command, in a palace crammed with works of art purchased from embarrassed Roman nobles, was to be found in the Palazzo Torlonia. A magnificent marble staircase rose from the vestibule in which stood Canova's great statue of Hercules. One hundred footmen in crimson and silver liveries and white wigs waited upon the eight hundred guests. There were three orchestras, in the ballroom, the long salon and in one of the galleries. To the music of Rossini a galaxy of beauty with diamonds, feathers and flowers swirled by. Venetian glass lit the ravishing scene, the candlelight giving fire to the diamonds and jewelled headdresses of the women.

Severn arrived with Lady Westmorland and Countess Potoca. Her ladyship looked superb, her head, a mass of curls, crowned by a dazzling parure. She wore prodigious diamond-earrings in the form of seahorses. She looked thirty, her creamy skin unlined, her slim figure tightly enswathed in white moiré silk with an overlay of Venetian lace. There was a discussion in groups as to whether she wore the famous Westmorland diamonds alleged to have been acquired by her husband, the old Earl who wanted to divorce her, from desperate French exiles who had fled to England during the Revolution. The Duc de Laval-Montmorency had been heard to declare that he had seen some of the jewels on the throat of Marie Antoinette and that they were part of the notorious necklace for which Cardinal de Rohan had ruined himself.

"If he saw them on Marie Antoinette he must have had second sight," commented Count d'Italinsky, the Russian Minister. "The Queen never dared to wear them. But diamonds like that are worth any scandal," he added, quizzing Lady Westmorland as she swept across the room.

The sensation of the evening in this glittering assembly was not Lady Westmorland. Soon after ten o'clock Mr and Mrs Bathurst arrived with their niece. Torlonia hurried forward to greet them at the foot of the grand staircase. They were watched by a hundred eyes, and there was a lull in the general chatter. Miss Bathurst was dressed wholly in white with a simple fillet of small red roses crowning her dark brown hair. The white silk dress enhanced the lustre of her eyes and the pink of her cheeks. Her grace of movement, a lyric of untroubled youth, drew the homage of men and women like.

"*Che persona adorabile!*" young Prince Altieri murmured to his companion.

It was observed that Torlonia gave her special attention. He presented half a dozen youths, scions of the Roman nobility. As they moved about her she laughed easily, and glided like a swan across the shining marble floor. In the ballroom she danced with nineteen-year-old Antonio Colonna, one of her riding companions in the Campagna.

Elton, faultlessly attired as always, flushed, with shining eyes, came across the floor and kissed Lady Westmorland's hand.

"I wonder what lucky devil will take her in to supper?" he said to Severn. "Rome's stunned!"

Madame Récamier went by on the arm of the Duc de Laval-Montmorency. They passed a small group containing Prince Jerome Bonaparte, his sister, ex-Queen Elise and his sister-in-law Hortense, ex-Queen of Holland. There were correct though restrained bows passed between the Bourbonists and the Bonapartists.

Elton was in paradise. He captured Miss Bathurst for the third time and led her to the floor.

"He will dance himself to death," said Gibson to Severn, when he left before dawn, with the orchestra still playing. "I must say he has every provocation."

Severn lingered on. It was five o'clock when he and Kirkup escorted Lady Westmorland to her palazzo. To Severn's dismay, she had no intention of going to bed. She ordered her carriage to wait. She knew an inn by Santa Sabina where they could breakfast and see the rising sun throw its first beam on the dome of St Peter's. After half an hour, having changed her gown, she descended and they set off towards the Tiber.

CHAPTER XI

I

ONE morning Elton called at Severn's studio bringing with him Miss Bathurst. It was the first time he had had the opportunity of meeting intimately the girl whose beauty had made a sensation in Rome. He found her as unaffected in manner as she was beautiful. With them came her uncle, Seymour Bathurst, attached to the British Embassy in Naples, a tall, aristocratic man, very reserved in manner. He and his wife were chaperoning their niece while Mrs Bathurst was away.

Severn found his young visitor even more alluring in her simple beauty than he had been led to expect by his glimpses of her at the Apponyi entertainment and the Torlonia ball. It was not men only who found this young Englishwoman possessed of such singular beauty. Women also succumbed to the adolescent charm she diffused so effortlessly. There was both a freshness and a fullness in her youthful figure. Her complexion and the expression of her eyes were dazzling, so that as Severn looked and spoke to her he became conscious of a singular sensation. He felt that he was beholding a miracle of Nature, fleeting doubtless, but something never to be forgotten. Her physical beauty was complemented by the radiance of her personality. The voice was exquisite in its soft tones. For her years she was unusually mature. Perhaps the event which had saddened her infancy and grown into her consciousness had contributed to this.

Severn could easily understand the rapture of his impressionable young friend Elton, who now seemed lifted to the seventh heaven of delight. The Bathursts approved of him, captivated by his youthful enthusiasm, his looks, his charm. He was having fierce competition from the young

Romans of family and wealth, with all the glamour of their names and tradition, but he was foremost in the regard of Rosa and her relations. They were both excellent equestrians. Almost every day a small cavalcade set forth from the Bathurst apartment near the Piazza di Spagna to ride in the Villa Borghese, in the meadows by the Tiber or farther afield in the Campagna, now entrancing with the early spring colouring.

It at once became Severn's ambition to have Rosa Bathurst sit for him but he knew that she was plagued by requests from artists, and he thought it prudent to defer his request. Owing to the increasing attentions of Elton and Kirkup, he had several opportunities of meeting her, either at parties for young people or at the various receptions that the Bathursts attended. Even Lady Westmorland showed enthusiasm over the new beauty invading Roman society. Falling more and more under the spell of this girl, Severn became conscious of the dullness of poor Maria. Graceful, warm, vivid, Rosa made every other girl seem colourless.

Wisely biding his time, Severn at last achieved his purpose. A date was made for her to give him sittings. His fear was that he might not prove equal to the opportunity. How could he convey her vital charm? There was a quality not wholly born of physical perfection, and its analysis defeated him.

One evening in the middle of March, a few days prior to the first sitting, he was cleaning his brushes preparatory to going out to dine with Gibson and Catherwood when Seymour Kirkup, without knocking, suddenly walked into the studio. Severn saw at once that he was greatly agitated. His first words expressed his emotion.

"Miss Bathurst's been drowned!" he cried.

"Drowned! It can't be true!" exclaimed Severn in shocked tones.

"Her horse slipped and fell with her into the Tiber."

"But when? How is it possible?"

"A little while ago Elton's man came to my place begging me to go at once to him. When I got there I found him quite prostrate. It took me some time to get a coherent story out of the poor fellow. He was sobbing like a child. It seems that in the late afternoon they all went out riding along the Tiber beyond the Ponte Molle—Miss Bathurst, her uncle and aunt, the Duc de Laval, Elton, Freeborn, Mills and Miss Sandon. They were on the way back when the Duc suggested another route he knew which took them on a bank above the river. The path was rather slippery after the thunderstorm last night and the Tiber just there has a swift current from the spring rains. It seems that the Duc got off his horse as the path narrowed and advised the others to do the same. Miss Bathurst and Miss Sandon felt quite confident and remained mounted. Rosa was riding Chestnut, her favourite, always a quiet mount. At one point the path became so narrow and difficult that her uncle, who had dismounted, became alarmed for her and attempted to take Chestnut's bridle. The horse threw up his head and at the same moment his hind legs slipped down the bank, which had crumbled. He made a vain attempt to recover himself and the bridle rein broke under the strain. Miss Bathurst fell backwards into the river with the horse over her. They disappeared for a few moments. Bathurst leapt in and swam around. The others on the bank, paralysed by the swiftness of the whole thing, saw Miss Bathurst and the horse rise to the surface for a moment and then disappear for ever. Bathurst, Elton and a groom swam about until they were exhausted. Boatmen are searching now, but so far no trace of Rosa or her horse has been found. The Tiber is flooded and very swift just there. It's too terrible! One just can't believe it! I made Elton get into

N

bed; his man could do nothing with him. He was chilled to the bone and demented with grief. I'm going back to him now. I've just called at the Bathursts. Naturally, they are in a terrible state. They tell me the old Duc's prostrate, lamenting that he's the cause of the tragedy through taking them that way, and he couldn't swim or do anything to help."

"I'll come with you to Elton's," said Severn. "What an incredible thing! And that lovely girl!"

He put on his hat and cloak. Darkness had fallen when they reached Elton's. With great effort, Severn checked the violent trembling of his limbs as they mounted to the apartment.

All Rome was stunned by the tragic death of Rosa Bathurst. In the few months of her sojourn her beauty and her happy disposition had made a complete conquest of Roman society. The tragedy hung over the city for several weeks. Some of the balls and receptions were cancelled for the gloom was prolonged by the failure to recover the poor girl's body. The carcase of the horse had been discovered downstream after five days. There was no sign of the rider. The Tiber seemed to have engulfed her forever. After a fortnight the search was abandoned. The memorial service was crowded by Catholics and non-Catholics. His Holiness sent his Cardinal-Secretary with a message of condolence to Mrs Bathurst, who had hurried to Rome on learning the tragic news.

The British colony had not recovered from the shock of this event when the Duchess of Devonshire died after a short illness. She had long been the recognised leader of the English community in Rome by virtue both of her rank and of her learning. An earl's daughter, a duke's widow, she had a commanding presence and an excellent mind. In her later years she had become more serious in purpose and had all Rome at her feet, ministers, cardinals, artists and Roman and English society. No one bothered to recall the fact that she had been the fifth Duke's mistress and had shared him with his first Duchess. At the end of her life she had distinguished herself by her excavations in the Forum and the printing of superb editions of Horace and Virgil. Every visitor of note to Rome went to her palazzo; not to be invited there was to miss the cachet that opened the doors of Roman Society. Perhaps, as Mr Ticknor observed, "she attempted to play the Maecenas a little too much," but she had been a generous patron of art and letters, a warm friend of Canova and Thorwaldsen. Her greatest friendship had been with Cardinal Consalvi, a flawless intimacy between a woman of culture and a prince of the Church. It was believed that she never recovered from the blow of his death.

"The Duchess's passing is a loss to our community," said Mrs Bunsen. The remark was singular, because in view of her past Mrs Bunsen regarded the Duchess as *déclassée* even in her second widowhood, though in her palazzo there was no gambling and the company was always decorous. To Severn her death was a misfortune. She had shown him great kindness, bought several of his paintings and conferred the distinction of her presence by repeated visits to his studio.

He had noticed at the Apponyi entertainment, when she had sat with her old friend Madame Récamier, that she looked sad and did not join in the general laughter. "Do come and see me, Mr Severn. I go out less and less," she had said to him on parting that evening. He felt regretful now that a series of small things had prevented him from calling during the last month. He knew that Lady Westmorland did not like him to be seen in the Devonshire camp since there was a coolness between the two ladies. The Duchess, usually very reserved in her opinions, had once spoken to him of Lady Westmorland as "your raffish friend." It was said with humorous intent, but the criticism was implied. On the death of Lady Davy, the Duchess had been the unrivalled hostess of Rome, as Lady Westmorland knew well. She had carried herself like an empress, living on a princely scale.

The woman who had been painted by Gainsborough and Reynolds, proposed to by Gibbon, and praised by Moore and Byron, apart from her rank as Duchess of Devonshire, had a fame proof against envy. It was not proof against gossip, as Severn soon learned. Before her body had been sealed in its coffin, Rome rang with a piquant scandal. Forgotten was the "affair" with Consalvi. A rumour long dormant concerning Georgiana and Elizabeth, firm friends and successive wives of the fifth Duke, raised its head again. The strangest allegations beat against the door of the death-chamber. Severn dismissed them as fantastic, but one day, at his studio, Miss Fairleigh made an appearance. True to form, she possessed the fullest information down to every detail of the singular events surrounding the mystery of the Duchess's last hours.

"You know that for days as she lay dying no one could get in to see her, not even her closest friends, Madame Récamier and the Duc de Laval?" said Miss Fairleigh, sipping her tea, and consciously staging a drama of mystery for her audience of seven. "Finally Madame Récamier wrote to the Duke of Devonshire, a serious, quiet young man, as you know, asking him when she might visit his stepmother. She got a polite note back putting her off, as also did the Duc de Laval. No one was able to get near the poor Duchess—the Duke mounted guard over the door all the time. Then one day Madame Récamier was summoned. When she arrived the Duc de Laval was also there. It was plain that the poor Duchess was near her end. She couldn't speak; all she could do was to press Madame Récamier's hand. The next day she was dead. The Duke sent her a ring which his stepmother had worn to the last moment and wished her to receive. She had a habit of giving rings, you know. Lord Byron told me she had given a diamond ring to his doctor, who had once cured Cardinal Consalvi of a serious illness."

Miss Fairleigh put down her teacup, nibbled a biscuit and asked Westmacott if she could have a little more air. He went to the window. She had deliberately suspended her story to heighten the effect, though she acted as if she had finished it.

"But why couldn't anyone get in to the Duchess?" asked Severn.

Miss Fairleigh smiled, straightened the lavender gloves in her lap and thanked her host for opening the window. Her audience waited impatiently for her to continue.

"It's almost incredible, but, I believe, true—no one could gain access to the Duchess," she said. "It is strange how things piece themselves together. You may remember Mr Bancroft, the nice young American who was here about fifteen months ago? When he was in Paris he dined with the American Minister, Mr Gallatin. Mr Gallatin conducted the negotiations for the Treaty of Ghent that ended the war between our country and his. After that he paid a visit to England and was much entertained. Among the houses he visited was Chatsworth. The young Duke had just inherited; he was about twenty-five. Gallatin took his son with him. He was a very handsome boy. David painted him quite naked, as Cupid embracing Psyche—much to his father's displeasure." Miss Fairleigh paused, took a sip of her tea and continued: "You musn't think I've lost the thread. It all pieces together marvellously," she said with enthusiasm.

"The American visited the Duke of Devonshire—the

present Duke?" asked young Eastlake, always particular.

"Yes, the present Duke. Well, one evening in the presence of Mr Gallatin and his son the Duke made an astonishing statement. The subject of marriage came up, and the Duke surprised them by saying quite solemnly, 'No son of mine will inherit the Dukedom. I shall never marry.' Coming from the handsomest and most eligible young bachelor in England, our richest Duke, it struck the Gallatins as an extraordinary statement, but obviously he wasn't joking. Mr Gallatin told Mr Bancroft the story. Mr Bancroft told me one day, when I said I was a friend of the Duchess. He asked me what Devonshire was like and whether it was true that he was a changeling, as the Gallatins had heard later."

"*Dio mio!* The plot thickens!" cried Elton, slapping his thigh. "Whose changeling?"

Miss Fairleigh looked across at Miss Lucas, whom she had brought with her. Miss Lucas had great renown from making ornate flower designs by sewing bleached fishbones on black velvet.

"It's rather indelicate. I don't know whether in mixed company I should proceed," said Miss Fairleigh, with every intention of proceeding.

"But the changeling—you mean to say he isn't the real Duke?" exclaimed Catherwood. "You can't leave us in suspense, Miss Fairleigh, and nothing you'll say can shock us!"

"Well, after Mr Bancroft's story I made a few inquiries. Of course, one mustn't accept mere gossip, but I think I have a few reasonable conclusions," said Miss Fairleigh. "To return to the difficulty of Madame Récamier and the Duc de Laval in getting to the Duchess, and Devonshire's peculiar behaviour, there are two theories. One is that the Duke has always been afraid that his stepmother might 'go over' to the Church. There's been quite a landslide lately. When people get old and want to know where they're going, the Catholic Church can give them positive assurance. It has it all firmly defined, whereas our theologians, I must admit, lifelong communicant of the Church of England that I am, with a Dean in the family, are somewhat wobbly. I had an aunt who became a disciple of Wesley, and I remember how she shocked her brother, the Dean, by telling him that she believed Wesley was right when he said that Marcus Aurelius would go to Heaven and sit down with Abraham and Isaac. You remember old Mrs Ashton, the Bishop's widow who died here last winter and 'went over' six months before she died, leaving everything to Cardinal Consalvi, for a Catholic orphans' home? Devonshire knew how intimate the Duchess was with the Cardinal and was afraid that her Protestantism might be shaken and she, too, would 'go over' at the end. Never having believed in anything for so long, it would be natural for her to want to make sure at the very end, poor thing. So Devonshire kept away anybody of the Catholic communion until she had lost her power of speech. The second theory, more simple, is that he would allow no one in her room in case, in contrition, she revealed her guilt."

"But what guilt? About the Duke being a changeling?" asked Severn.

"Of course!" responded Miss Fairleigh.

"Then who is he if he isn't the real Duke? What a funny business!" exclaimed Elton.

"Ah, that's the point! The story is this—mind you, I don't vouch for it," continued Miss Fairleigh. "The first Duchess, Georgiana, the great beauty, and Elizabeth Foster, who became Duchess after her death, were close friends. They lived together in Devonshire House with the fifth Duke. The relationship was said to be very peculiar. There were children of various parentage running all over the house, according to report. The essential thing was that the Duchess Georgiana should produce an heir to the Dukedom. She took to her bed at the same time as her friend, Lady Elizabeth Foster—Mr Foster was no longer living with her—for the same reason. When unluckily Georgiana's child proved to be a girl and Lady Elizabeth's a boy, it was a simple matter to make the exchange. It seems the present Duke knows he is the changeling and that he was at his mother's and not his stepmother's deathbed! Hence his desire to keep everyone away. He was afraid the dying woman would reveal her secret."

"But it couldn't be much of a secret if he had already told the Gallatins," observed Kirkup.

"Mr Bancroft did not say that the Gallatins had said the Duke revealed to them that he was a changeling. The Duke said that he would never marry and have a son to inherit. He possibly said it in an unguarded moment. It was from others that the Gallatins learned the reason for this singular statement made at Chatsworth. Anyhow, that's the story. The Duke's behaviour has certainly been very odd!"

"If we live long enough and Devonshire keeps his vow, we'll be able to credit the story," said Eastlake.

"*Dio mio!* That's perilous reasoning for all of us bachelors!" cried Catherwood.

The company broke into laughter.

II

Lady Westmorland, discussing the rumour the next day in Severn's studio, was certain that the story was true. "I've always said that Devonshire's the image of the Duchess. I expect Thou Shalt Nott knows the truth."

"Who?"

"Thou Shalt Nott is Byron's nickname for the Reverend

Dr Nott, her favourite parson here. When that strange collection, the Shelleys and the Williamses, were living in the same palazzo at Pisa, across the Arno from Byron, Dr Nott lived on the ground floor, where he conducted services for the English colony. Shelley at that time was running after Mrs Williams, as she called herself, for she was the mistress of Mr Williams. There was some coolness between Shelley and his wife because of his attentions to Jane Williams. His rapture over the abduction of Mary Godwin was long over, and Mrs Shelley's crazy husband began to bore her. So she sought consolation. Dr Nott, learning that she was the daughter of the revolutionary, Godwin, as well as the wife of Shelley the atheist, preached a special sermon, directed at her, upon the wickedness of atheists. It was too much for her, and highly indignant at the attack on Shelley, her father and herself, she would never allow Dr Nott to come upstairs again. Byron wagged a finger at him, I was told, and said, 'Thou shalt, Nott, bear false witness.' The Reverend Doctor attended the poor Duchess in her last hours."

"Did you ever meet Shelley? He was an angel of kindness," said Severn.

"No. He was mad, but of course you must be grateful to him in view of what he wrote about you."

She pointed to the words from *Adonais* he had rewritten on the wall of his studio. "He certainly walked about like an angel."

"What do you mean?"

"I have a friend with a villa at Lerici. She told me that Shelley, and that brigand Trelawny, who frightened us all here, used to swim quite naked. One day when she lunched at their house—just a boatman's hovel—Shelley came in and walked through the dining-room without a rag on him. They seemed to think nothing of it!" said Lady Westmorland, laughing. "But my friend found no wings on him! I saw Mrs Shelley, very sad and battered, poor thing, a year ago, when I went to call on Lord Byron at Genoa, just before he went off to Greece. She was living in another villa with the Leigh Hunts. That reminds me. Lord Holland's boy was there. He has written from the Egmonts at Petworth to say he is coming to Rome next winter. He's a most charming boy. You will like him. I see another patron for you!" said Lady Westmorland with a smile.

III

The early Roman spring came in with its riot of roses, its walls bright with cascades of pink geraniums and purple bougainvillæa. The air grew heavy with the scent of orange blossom and then, almost before its loveliness had been apprehended, the heat came and held Rome in somnolence. That summer, with the city emptied of its residents and visitors, brought three sensations. In May came the news of Lord Byron's death at Missolonghi. Though he had died of fever, his end had seemed worthy and heroic. He had laid down his life in the cause of Greek liberty, and once again all Europe rang with his name. It was a dramatic end, a perfect apotheosis for a bizarre figure that had dazzled the world. So three of England's greatest poets, Keats, Shelley, Byron, known to the Italian scene, had perished within the space of three years. The thought made Severn feel like a survivor from a dead age.

He was preparing to leave for Genzano in the Alban Hills, to escape the heat and to paint the spectacular peasants there, when he was stunned by the news of the death of Maria Walker's mother. She had been returning in a gig from an excursion in the Campagna. Outside the Porta San Paolo the horse had shied, overturning the gig and throwing Mrs Walker and the groom into the fosse. When the groom got to his feet, half-stunned, and went to his mistress, he found she was dead, her neck broken by the fall. Most of the Walkers' friends had left Rome. The necessary arrangements fell upon Severn, who did all he could for the two distraught sisters. After the funeral Maria and Julia decided to return to an aunt in England. He escorted them as far as Civitavecchia, where they embarked for London. Maria passed out of his life.

In July Severn went to Genzano, and had only been there a short time when he got a despairing note from Elton. Rosa Bathurst's body had been found in a sandy bed of the Tiber. It was in a state of extraordinary preservation, her features unchanged since the day the Tiber had engulfed her. Elton implored Severn to return to Rome to go with him to the funeral. So two days later they both went to the Protestant Cemetery and stood on the slope a few yards below Shelley's grave and saw the ill-fated English girl whose beauty had hypnotised Rome lowered to sleep among her countrymen. The Bathursts were away in England. In the little group of mourners standing there in the early dawn only five friends who had known her in the flower of youth were present, the Duc de Laval-Montmorency. Mr Freeborn, Mr Mills, Elton, all witnesses of the tragedy, and Severn.

In October Severn came back from the Alban Hills. Lady Westmorland had returned. He found her in new quarters.

She had moved from the Villa Negroni to the vast Palazzo Rospigliosi which rose behind a high wall in a big courtyard a few hundred yards from the Pope's residence, the Quirinal. An army of workmen laboured to renovate the series of magnificent salons. The palace stood on the site of the Baths of Constantine and had been built in 1603 by Cardinal Scipione Borghese who had demolished the baths for building material. Cardinal

Mazarin had employed Maderno to decorate it, and from his time it had been the seat of the French Ambassadors. This gave Lady Westmorland her clue. She invoked the advice of the Duc de Laval-Montmorency, the friend of Madame de Staël and Chateaubriand's rival for the love of Madame Récamier. He was a little bald one-eyed man with exquisite manners and rapier wit. Lady Westmorland decided that a *settecento* ballroom must be converted into a Louis Seize one, as she had eighty gilt chairs of that era. Severn was to decorate the panels with medallions of French statesmen, poets and musicians. He vehemently protested that he knew nothing of these French celebrities and that medallions were not his *métier*. It was in vain. She insisted and he began the cartoons in despair when, happily, the landlord, Prince Rospigliosi, forbade any change in Cardinal Mazarin's decorations. For two months workmen had possessed the palace.

Early in November Lady Westmorland's friend, Henry Edward Fox, a delicate-looking youth of twenty-two, arrived in Rome. She gave a dinner in his honour to which she invited forty guests. Severn was among them. Later she brought Fox to his studio. He was elegant and somewhat patronising in manner. It was clear that, an aristocrat, the future Lord Holland, he believed in keeping people in their places. Mr Severn, he felt, gave himself airs, and, despite Lady Westmorland's opinion, he did not think him a very good artist.

Whatever Mr Fox thought of Mr Joseph Severn he had no mean opinion of himself. His background was as curious as it was distinguished. He was the son and heir of Lord Holland. His mother was one of the great hostesses of London, reigning at Holland House, famous for its salon.

Henry Fox was lucky to be the heir, family events considered. His mother, formerly Lady Webster, had been the wife of a baronet twenty-three years older than herself. Sir Godfrey Webster had married her, the sixteen-year-old heiress to a West Indian property with a revenue of seven thousand pounds a year. It was not a happy marriage. Sir Godfrey had a violent temper and wanted a quiet life, while she wanted a gay one. They had five children, two dying soon after birth. In 1794 they were in Florence when they met a party of young Englishmen, Lord Granville, Mr Leveson-Gower, Lord Wycombe and Lord Holland, the nephew of Charles James Fox, making the Grand Tour. Sir Godfrey departed for England a year later and Lord Holland and Lady Webster then travelled openly together. They returned to England the following year.

It was Lady Webster's intention to get a divorce and marry Holland, her lover. This required a special Parliamentary Bill. After much delay, she obtained it—at a price. Sir Godfrey stipulated that he should receive six thousand pounds damages and retain all of her income except £800 a year. The judge denounced the terms as iniquitous, but the parties privately agreed to them. Four months before the divorce was granted Lady Webster gave birth to a son which the guilty couple openly acknowledged.

There was another singular fact. A year after Sir Godfrey's departure from Florence, Lady Webster had written to inform him that their infant daughter, Harriet, had died of measles in Modena. It was untrue. Fearing to lose the child after the break with her husband, it had been concealed by her. She had arranged in Modena a mock funeral with a kid buried in the coffin instead of the child. She took the daughter to England when she went there with Lord Holland. Two years after the divorce she decided to make a confession and to restore the child to Sir Godfrey, as he had begun to make inquiries in the matter.

The Hollands went abroad after five years' residence in

England, where Lady Holland had created a salon but had failed to be received into Society except by the Duchess of Devonshire and Lady Bessborough. The Hollands moved to Paris, where Henry, the legitimate heir, was born. Back in England in 1805, Lady Holland by her talents and effrontery, and Lord Holland by his progressive political views, succeeded in creating a salon at Holland House that rivalled the beautiful Lady Jersey's. They aroused much criticism by their Bonapartism. Lord Holland had visited Murat in Naples, opposed a Bill for the detention of Napoleon, and later moved for papers relating to his treatment on St Helena. Lady Holland shared this pro-Bonapartism. She visited Napoleon at Malmaison, she consoled him over his exile on Elba, and sent him parcels and sweets. Napoleon, in turn, bequeathed to her a gold snuff-box. The incident provoked a scuffle in verse between two noble poets. Lord Carlisle, shocked at her acceptance of the legacy only six years after Waterloo, addressed some admonitory lines to her:

> *Lady, reject this gift 'tis tinged with gore!*
> *Those crimson spots a dreadful tale relate.*
> *It has been grasped by an Infernal Power*
> *And by the hand which sealed young Enghien's fate.*

Byron could not resist an ironic retort:

> *Lady, accept the gift a hero wore*
> *In spite of all this elegiac stuff;*
> *Let not seven stanzas written by a bore*
> *Prevent your ladyship from taking snuff.*

Delighted, Lady Holland took Lord Byron's advice. She had wit, beauty and vivacity, but she had no tact. Her rudeness amounted to genius. When Mr Samuel Rogers talked too much at her salon she said: "Your poetry is bad enough. Be sparing of your prose."

Such was the mother of the youth who now arrived in Rome. Her championship of Napoleon opened for him all the doors of the Bonaparte clan. Lady Westmorland was enchanted with this good-looking youth. Gratitude to his mother also enhanced him in her sight, for Lady Holland had been outspoken about Lord Westmorland's tenure of the Lord Lieutenancy of Ireland. "His lordship's manners are those that spring from powers engrafted on a low education, and his language is a symbol of both," she had said; and when the quarrel broke out between him and his wife some years later, Lady Holland accused him of creating evidence, hoping thereby to confine Lady Westmorland to an asylum, in order to avoid the expense of a separate maintenance.

With the advent of young Fox, Severn receded into the background. Lady Westmorland sought to possess Fox, but was quickly shown her mistake by this cool young man. He was welcomed at once by Louis, the ex-King of Holland, by Hortense, his wife who lived apart, by Prince Canino, and by Prince Jerome, ex-King of Westphalia. Within three weeks he received a favour rarely accorded to an Englishman. He was received by Madame Mère in the seclusion of the Palazzo Bonaparte. Madame Mère had outlawed all of the British race since Lord Londonderry had ignored Pius VII's appeal for clemency in the treatment of her son. Lord Holland's son was in another category.

He waited on her, dressed in the correct attire prescribed by her chamberlain—black knee-breeches, white silk stockings, a blue court-coat, white gloves and plumed hat. She received him seated, with her brother Cardinal Fesch and two ladies-in-waiting. On the walls behind her were portraits and busts; her husband, Charles Bonaparte, her five sons, Joseph, Napoleon, Lucien, Louis and Jerome, her three daughters Elise, Pauline and Caroline.

These were all by the supreme artists of the age, Gérard, Isabey, David and Bartolini.

Fox discovered that Madame Mère spoke appalling French with a strong Corsican accent. The room was heavily curtained and dark, but the little old lady had the bearing of a queen. After a brief talk and kind inquiries concerning Lord and Lady Holland, she dismissed him. Before departing, Cardinal Fesch conducted him into a neighbouring room. It was lined with black velvet and lit by only two torches. There were three busts on pedestals: Canova's excellent likeness of Madame Mère, his bust of Napoleon, and one of the little King of Rome, the last object Napoleon had gazed at from his death-bed three years earlier.

Fox dined that night with Lady Westmorland. It was a small party of six, including Severn, to whom he made himself unusually agreeable. He stayed in Rome another month, and then departed for Naples. Six months passed before Severn saw him again. He wrote to Lady Westmorland gossipy accounts of his life, which she related to Severn. He had found the Blessingtons installed in a magnificent palazzo, living in princely style, with Lady Blessington holding court and D'Orsay in attendance. A friendship between the two young men was renewed.

IV

June came with a wave of heat. Lady Westmorland moved to a villa lent to her at Gaeta, the medieval town on a promontory halfway between Rome and Naples. She invited Severn to accompany her. There was a house party of ten in a lovely villa with a terraced garden going down to the Mediterranean.

Before Severn left Rome he received a letter from Charles Armitage Brown in Florence: "Pauline Borghese died here two days ago in Prince Camillo's palazzo. His

Duchess friend considerately moved out when Pauline came here to die. They were reconciled at the last. It is said he was in tears, and she said, 'Forgive me all the trouble I've given you.' She died of cancer of the stomach, like Napoleon, aged forty-five. They say her last word was 'Napoleon.' *Sic transit.*"

Gaeta was an easy distance from Naples on the Via Appia, past Formia where Cicero was assassinated. They found Fox in rooms on the Vomero not far from the magnificent Palazzo Belvedere, in which the Blessingtons were installed. Severn fell under the spell of this lovely, intelligent woman. She told him much about Byron and read to him some of her Journal based on talks in Genoa just before he sailed for Greece. They discussed Trelawny, who after Byron's death had married a Greek girl and was living in a cavern sumptuously fitted out, reached only by ladders, on Mount Parnassus. He had survived a murderous attempt on his life by a treacherous English colleague and was buying Turkish slaves and setting them free. A visitor from Greece had brought Lady Blessington this account.

The handsome Count D'Orsay had charmed Naples. He rode by Lady Blessington's carriage, splendidly mounted, when they went to the evening Corso. Lord Blessington spent his time sailing the *Bolivar*, bought from Byron at Genoa. Severn found D'Orsay as delightful as ever. Fox was often one of the trio they made for riding. He was saddened to learn from Cotterill, still banking in Naples, that his sister, who had been so ill on that voyage from London to Naples in the *Maria Crowther*, had succumbed to her disease.

One day young Henry Fox jubilantly confided in him about his affair with Teresa Guiccioli. Byron's mistress was living in Naples, basking in the glamour of her association with the poet. She could not determine whether to adopt a pose of romantic mourning or to indulge her thirst for amorous adventure. The red-headed young Countess, who had hypnotised Bancroft on his visit to Byron at Leghorn three years ago was now twenty-five. Fox, unselectively amorous in the heat of youth, had found conquest easy. For a time the association had been passionate, but by September Fox was tiring of the affair.

"My dear Severn, as you see, she's pretty eyes, a lovely skin, a caressing voice, and is turbulently passionate. But I find her rather gross and carnal, and what irritates me is her ridiculous talk about fidelity. She believes she's deeply in love and is always chattering about constancy! And she will try to be clever because she's lived with Byron. Three days ago we went over to Nisida and landed in my favourite bay there. It was a perfect night, warm, with a play of summer lightning over the mountains—idyllic for an affair—but no! She became temperamental, talked about the moon on the Grand Canal at Venice when Byron took her out—sacred memories she must not sully—which she's been sullying for a month!"

"How did you start all this?" asked Severn.

The excited youth threw up his arms. "How does one start these things? I met her; she asked me to call on her. We sat on her balcony and talked. There was a full moon over the Bay—Vesuvius aglow in the sky. Byron said, 'There's nothing like the moon for mischief.' How true! She listened and consented, as we looked at the moonlight on the water. But not then, the next night! So I returned, and had somewhat of a surprise. She received me with the deliberation of a woman who makes it not only her pleasure but her trade. I suppose I'll soon get over it, but she's making preposterous claims—can't live without me, and no one must know!"

"How old are you?"

"Twenty-three," said Fox.

"I'm almost nine years your senior. That doesn't give me years of wisdom, but I can tell you something. Why do you criticise her morals when you show no moral control yourself? We men are one-sided. We want our women virginal if possible—anyhow, frail enough for us to vent our appetites on—and then we hold them in reprobation because they satisfy us! You're not complaining, I hope, that the Countess seduced you?"

Fox looked at Severn, surprised. "Since you put it like that, I shouldn't complain. But does your philosophy bar your affairs?" he asked.

"I'm not complaining, nor remarking on my affairs."

"Too much of a gentleman, eh?" commented Fox with a faint sneer. "And what is your line with D'Orsay, Blessington and her ladyship? There's a nice state of affairs for you!"

"I find them hospitable. I don't care to sit in judgment on anybody," said Severn in a tone that closed the discussion.

V

They were all back in Rome in November. Severn went with Lady Westmorland to see the Borghese Chapel in Santa Maria Maggiore where Pauline Borghese had been laid to rest. She surprised him by saying, "It's the only faith to die in. Look what a gorgeous setting!"

"They borrowed another man's sepulchre for Christ. Does it matter where one's disposed of? Surely the simpler the better?" said Severn.

"Of course it matters! I would rather rest in St Peter's than anywhere else on earth!" retorted Lady Westmorland.

"Then your ladyship must set about qualifying."

"Don't scoff! I find the Catholic religion very enticing. One has a part in the great Christian tradition."

Severn changed the subject. He had no desire to debate with her, aware how soon she became ill-tempered when challenged.

That same day, in the company of Fox, he took her to call on Westmacott. He was at work on a memorial to Rosa Bathurst for erection in the Protestant Cemetery. It was a simple cenotaph with a long inscription in English and Italian on either side that set forth a widow's and a mother's grief. It was almost a protest against Fate that had robbed her of a husband of twenty-six and of an only child of sixteen: "Oh you who read this story of affliction and of sorrow take warning of the instability of human happiness!"

"You cannot imagine what trouble Mrs Bathurst has given me," said Westmacott as they read the long inscription. "Who will ever bother to read all that? Who'll remember what happened to poor Rosa? But it might have been worse. Mrs Bathurst wrote me that she wanted to have Rosa flying up to Heaven, with Mr Bathurst seated on a cloud to receive her. She said in a postscript that Mr Bathurst resembled Antinous! With much patience I got it down as simple as this, and with much self-sacrifice also, for the other design would have cost her twice as much. Will posterity thank me? No!"

There was a large reception at Torlonia's that evening. When the Countess Guiccioli came into the salon Fox moved hurriedly behind Severn. "We've quarrelled. I don't want to see her," he said. She was saluted very warmly by the ex-King of Sardinia, Victor Emmanuel. The most beautiful woman there was his daughter, the Duchess of Lucca. Severn had made a miniature of her a year ago. She greeted him with much cordiality. Fox was with young Lord Dudley Stuart. He presented them to the Duchess. For some reason she became suddenly very reserved and soon moved away. Severn was distressed and puzzled. It was Fox who enlightened him when they returned together from seeing Lady Westmorland home. Stuart had had a liaison with Prince Canino's lovely daughter, Christine, and a child had been born to them while she was married to Count de Posse. Her marriage was now annulled and she had married Stuart. The scandal had shaken the Bonaparte clan, and by many of them and their friends she was not received.

When Severn got home that evening he found Gibson waiting for him. Surprised, he soon learned the reason.

"Severn, I've sad news for you. I've just heard from Montpellier that poor Elton died there last Tuesday. It was a merciful release, poor lad. There had been no hope really since last July. How we shall all miss him!"

It was the heaviest blow Severn had suffered since Keats had gone. He had not seen Elton since he had left for Naples that summer. At their last meeting he had noticed that he was not well and had grown ominously thinner. "It's the heat," he said. "So I'm off to the French Alps." He was as elegant and debonair as ever, but Severn knew how heavily he had been hit by the tragic death of Rosa Bathurst. For a month after the tragedy he had ridden up and down the Tiber's banks hoping that he might find the poor girl's body. He had completely broken down after the funeral. Severn recalled how vivacious he had been that morning when he had brought Rosa to the studio. Weak in some ways, he had always been unselfish, cheerful and lovable.

CHAPTER XII

I

SEVERN put down his brushes. The light went early these November days. When he had changed he waited for Eastlake who was going with him to Lady Westmorland's. She had just returned from Lausanne with Henry Fox. All the past nine months she had been more restless and erratic than ever with visits to Paris, Florence, Naples and Lausanne in the summer and autumn.

As he waited for Eastlake, Severn reviewed the recent months of his life. With young Fox on the scene her ladyship had not been so possessive. Yet he must not be ungrateful to her, though she was often wildly exasperating. He owed much to her for the miraculous change in his life these last five years. He had arrived in Rome an unknown artist, with a dying friend. He was almost penniless and desperately hoping to win the Royal Academy Travelling Pension by which he alone could exist. In Rome on their arrival they had not known a soul. When he had stood by Keats's grave in that early dawn five years ago only three persons he knew were present, and they were all new acquaintances. Now in this year of grace, 1826, he was established as an artist, he had as many commissions as he could complete, a host of good friends among his fellow artists, and also the standing of a Royal Academy Award winner.

On the social side his life had become a fairy tale. He was invited into the palaces of all the English aristocracy in Rome, the holders of great names he had only heard of back in England. It was difficult in writing home, describing his life, to keep out of his letters the procession of people with resounding titles in order to avoid the charge of snobbery. In addition to this English society, he had come to know many of the Roman nobility that mingled with the English colony, the Massimo, Doria, Colonna, Aldobrandini and other great princely houses. To these could be added the diplomats attached to the Holy See, many of whom he met at the Bunsens, always a sober element, and at Lady Westmorland's, always a frivolous element. There was also his wide acquaintance among the Bonaparte clan that straddled Roman society through its marriages and the Pope's benevolence towards these deposed kings, queens, princes and princesses of a *nouvelle royauté déguenillée*, as the Duc de Laval-Montmorency, the official representative of the restored Bourbons, always derisively called it.

Severn suffered no illusions regarding his penetration of these high circles. It was certainly not due to his eminence as an artist. If they bought his works, it was not from any great appreciation of them. They went to artists' studios as they went to the faro tables, as a diversion—one of many in this ageless city where everybody moved in the atmosphere of a fancy-dress ball. His social position was nil, his bourgeois origin known. His extraordinary success had been due to a number of factors. The first was Lady Westmorland's virtual adoption of him, to the amusement of her friends, genial or malicious, as the mood took them. She kept him always at her side, possessive, assertive, but on the whole well-intentioned. She was a formidable woman, gifted, erratic, beautiful, rich, and tempestuous at times. Nothing impaired her zest for life. In addition to her interest in him, which had advanced him socially and artistically, he possessed extreme good looks, youth, a quick mind and an indefatigably cheerful disposition. "The Cockney coxcomb" one disagreeable Society woman had called him, but in the end she succumbed to his charm and good manners. In one respect he showed good sense. He never presumed upon his position or assets. He was never put out by any slight others would have resented. He never gossiped unkindly or failed to perform his duty as an agreeable guest. His difficulty, increasing every day, was to reserve something of his time for artistic labour and to keep Lady Westmorland's monopoly within bounds that enabled him to fulfil his serious purpose in Rome.

He retained one other attraction, as he well knew, and it was this factor that now occupied his mind as he sat in his study and watched the enchantment of the sunset fading over Rome. He was almost thirty-three and still unattached. It was something that poor Elton, in common with many others, had always wondered at. How could a young man with such a presence and a social nature escape the arrows of Cupid? The natural physical impulses of youth had no lack of opportunity here in Rome, particularly in the artistic circles, as dozens of *ménages* up and down the Via Margutta gave proof. There had been Elton's promiscuity, increased, it would seem, by the reproductive urge of the disease that threatened him. There was Kirkup's frailty, expressed in a number of liaisons with scarcely reputable partners.

Two months ago Kirkup had gone into hiding from a termagant he had installed in his apartment. She was a girl of eighteen, actually picked off a fruit-barrow in the populous Trastevere district, renowned for the violence of its occupants. He had imported her to pose as Ariadne. She had remained to rule as Xantippe. On his attempt to evict her, following his protest against her desire to play hostess to a horde of brothers, sisters, cousins and acquaintances, she had burned all her clothes and defied him to put her out *tutto nudo*. A forcible attempt with a blanket had resulted in a wolfish bite of his hand, a scratched face and the use of vocal organs that would have dominated an opera chorus. It had been a strange sequence to an elegant dinner party that he had graced at the Palazzo Colonna where Hortense, ex-Queen of Holland, and Madame Récamier had been his table partners. Persuasion, reinforced by fifty *scudi*, had enabled Severn to get rid of the virago. If the story related by Brown concerning Byron's life in Venice were true, Kirkup's and Byron's tastes were much alike.

Severn read Kirkup a lesson. It was taken to heart for a time. "Why am I so weak when these damned houris look at me? You are right, Severn. It's undignified. It's got to stop!" said Kirkup. But the attempt at dignity did not last a month. One evening, calling at Kirkup's studio, he found him on a divan with a tawny creature who was posing for "Phryne descending to the bath." She was in a condition for the bath, but instead of posing she was eating cherries out of a basket. Kirkup had hung a pair on her ears and was endeavouring to bite them with much play and laughter when Severn walked in. One never knew what Kirkup might do next. His artistic output was fitful. Driven by necessity, he might have been an excellent artist. He seemed in a fair way to be ruined by an adequate private income, as was so often the case.

Severn's mind went back to his own emotional life. There had been a series of pleasant affairs, but none of them had impelled him into matrimony. There was Miss Fawcett, now barely a memory. Miss Carlow had attracted him for a few weeks. They had gone about Rome together, danced and met at receptions, but when she announced her departure it was the loss of an agreeable companion that he regretted, no more. Then Maria had attracted him. It had been a longer and more intimate affair. The Walker home, to one so homeless, had some of the qualities he had missed greatly since he had left England. The two sisters were bright, amiable girls. That summer at Naples was memorable. Propinquity, the romantic setting of the terraced garden by the sea, the moonlight shining through the vine pergola, the lapping of water, the warm, starlit nights, had all created an idyllic background to their youth. Then the languor of the timeless days began to pall. Sweet Maria had no volition. Lady Westmorland had named her failing with cruel insight: dear Maria, so good-natured, so equable, was insipid.

The news of Shelley's death had aroused Severn from a stupor of dreaming hours. Naples suddenly became a lotos land where one's ambition became drugged. He had fled, and it had never been the same again. The vital loveliness of Rosa Bathurst had made Maria even more colourless. Her departure after Mrs Walker's death had removed the uneasy memory of a blunder he had almost committed. The truth was that he had only one commanding interest, his painting. That was mistress, wife and family to him. His mind rebelled at Kirkup's alternative.

A tap on the door broke his reverie as he sat by the window. It was Eastlake who apologised for his lateness.

"I've kept the carriage. We can ride over to the Rospigliosi. I've got a good idea what her ladyship wants us for. She's planning a big musical party. Madame Vestris is going to recite from *Childe Harold*. I'm going to sing, and you will play a duet with her ladyship."

"God forbid! I should die of fright. I can't perform in public," exclaimed Severn.

"Taglioni's orchestra's been engaged. I've just seen him in the Greco. So you know what you're in for!"

When they arrived at the Palazzo Rospigliosi there was not a sign of life. The majordomo showed them into a small salon lit by one candelabra. They waited. There was nothing to read. When half an hour had gone by,

Eastlake became impatient. "I'm going to ring and ask if we're expected," he said, rising.

His hand was on the bell-rope when the door opened. But it was not Lady Westmorland. It was a strange young woman, in her twenties possibly. She stood shyly in the doorway for a moment and then moved forward.

"I'm Elizabeth Montgomerie," she said. "Lady Westmorland has asked me to apologise for her delay. She is dressing for a dinner at the Austrian Embassy. She will be down in a few moments."

They could see her more clearly now as the candlelight lit her face. She was clad simply in white muslin that clung to her slim figure and virgin bosom. Her hair fell in dark curls, framing a small round face. She had rosy cheeks and candid blue eyes below a wide brow with clearly defined eyebrows, slightly arched. She was extremely shy. In that dark small salon with the heavy damask curtains and painted ceiling she looked elf-like.

It was a few minutes before conversation became easy. Aware that they were puzzled, she explained her presence. She was Scottish, as her accent denoted. She had come from Scotland to be with Lady Westmorland who had adopted her. She had never been abroad before.

"Do you like Rome?" asked Severn after a pause.

"Oh, yes, but I have seen very little of it yet," she answered.

There was another awkward pause. The two young men felt tongue-tied but presently they induced her to talk in response to their questions about her journey. Eastlake decided she was not more than twenty-two or so. Her voice was low and musical, but she spoke with much nervousness and had a marked Scots accent. Her hands never rested. She continually watched the door. A somewhat strained half-hour went by. At last footsteps sounded on the stone floor. She abruptly checked her words and rose. Lady Westmorland came in arrayed like a queen, her throat and bosom sparkling with diamonds. She offered her hand for their salutes and made no reference to her delay.

"You have met Miss Montgomerie? I hope she has not bored you," she said, glancing at the girl.

"Oh no. It has been most pleasant for us," answered Eastlake.

"Elizabeth, you may go. I have business with these gentlemen," she said, seating herself.

The girl silently withdrew. Severn smiled at her as he held the door for her, but she did not raise her eyes.

"It is about the concert I am planning," began Lady Westmorland. "You must both help me. Here is a programme I've drawn up. You, Mr Eastlake, will sing two songs—two of those you sang so admirably at Lady Dewhurst's one evening. Mr Severn, we are going to play a duet."

It was in vain that they protested. Of course they would help her, she insisted. After some fifteen minutes' discussion, she said she must leave. She took them in her carriage as far as the Piazza Barberini. Severn made one reference to Miss Montgomerie, asking whether she would be long in Rome.

"Inevitably. She is an orphan and has no other place but with me. I hope she will prove a useful companion, but I fear she has little sense."

When she had driven on, Eastlake gave vent to his feelings.

"I'm damned if I'll sing for her! I shall have a Roman fever. The way she talks of that poor girl! I could strangle that woman at times! Why do we all tolerate her?" he cried.

"Because she has rank, wit, beauty, wealth, and the skin of a hippopotamus," answered Severn.

Severn slept fitfully that night. He kept thinking of the girl Lady Westmorland had treated so rudely. He could see her face now, its gentle beauty, its air of sadness. He wondered what tragedy had touched her. Two days later, at a rehearsal in the Palazzo Rospigliosi, he looked for her, but she made no appearance. At the concert he saw her again but only for a few minutes. They spoke, still very shy with each other. She smiled at something he said, revealing beautiful small teeth. The general effect on him was to awaken a sense of protection, a desire to make her feel less restrained and to trust him. It was absurd, for he hardly knew her. Instinctively, he felt that Lady Westmorland would not tolerate his interest in her ward. She seemed seldom to go out with her. In ten days he saw her only once in the carriage with her guardian. She had said Lady Westmorland had adopted her. There must be a story behind that. No one seemed to know for what reason she had adopted this girl.

Later the reason became clearer. Miss Montgomerie was called on to do a hundred odd jobs; some of them seemed more suitable for a maid to perform. She appeared never to give satisfaction to her guardian, who was in a constant state of irritation with her. She was subject to minor humiliations. Sometimes she dined at the table, but was ignored in the conversation. Lady Westmorland showed resentment if the girl had attention paid to her by the guests. There was a painful scene one evening when they were playing faro. Miss Montgomerie sat sewing in one of the windows, for Lady Westmorland never allowed her to gamble, which seemed only proper. Desiring a wrap, for the evening was chilly, she sent her ward to her boudoir. When she came back with a yellow silk shawl Lady Westmorland flung it angrily on a chair.

"Why should you imagine I can wear a yellow wrap

with a blue dress? Will you ever show any sense?" she cried loudly, in front of her guests.

The girl stood silent for a moment, the blood mantling her cheeks.

"I am sorry, Lady Westmorland. What colour do you wish?" she asked, picking up the wrap.

"If you'd any sense you would know. Certainly not yellow," retorted Lady Westmorland.

Miss Montgomerie left the room. Severn was so uncomfortable that he could not concentrate on the game.

One evening, exasperated by another scene, he left early. Lady Westmorland had behaved like a fishwife.

II

That spring he held an exhibition jointly with Eastlake and Kirkup at "the British Academy of Rome," as his long studio was called. He invited Lady Westmorland to a little soirée he was giving for the opening.

"I have not asked Miss Montgomerie, but I do hope that your ladyship will bring her," said Severn.

"The girl has no appreciation of painting. It would be a waste of time, Mr Severn," she said.

"Miss Montgomerie seems quite interested in art when I talk to her. Do please bring her."

"Very well. Since you have such a high opinion of Elizabeth, I will bring her."

When they came it was Lady Westmorland who dominated the scene. Miss Montgomerie wore an enchanting lilac bonnet that emphasized her exquisite little face. He could not refrain from complimenting her on her appearance. She was in a state of excitement and talked and laughed with a group of young artists that gathered about her. After only twenty minutes Lady Westmorland announced her departure. Severn was certain that it was because she could not bear to see Miss Montgomerie paid so much attention by his friends.

"The old cat won't let the kitten play!" said Catherwood. "What a lovely girl! Peaches and cream—whipped up with vinegar."

Throughout the summer Miss Montgomerie and Severn met intermittently but briefly. She remained very shy. It was plain that she was unhappy. The winter season in Rome was brilliant. Prince Torlonia surpassed himself with a masked ball for eight hundred guests. He put up a silk pavilion covering the whole of the inner courtyard to make a vast conservatory with fountains and an orchestra embowered in a great basket of flowers suspended from the ceiling. The Duc de Laval-Montmorency gave a dinner party with covers for eighty. Lady Westmorland created a ludicrous incident at the card table, taking offence at a story the Ambassador told about two gentlemen bathing naked who saw a lady fall in the river and went to her rescue. When they pulled her out one said, "*Pardonnez-moi, madame, de n'avoir pas de gants.*" The company laughed. Lady Westmorland rose haughtily, expressed her displeasure and asked for her carriage. Poor Miss Montgomerie, dancing in the gallery, was dragged away.

III

Spring brought a great influx of visitors. Severn was depressed by the departure of Kirkup early that year. He was settling in Florence. Ewing had stayed on in England. Elton had died; now Kirkup went out of his life. All three had been very close to him since Keats's death. But a new interest had come into his life. The more he saw of Elizabeth Montgomerie the more she occupied his thoughts. Yet he had many misgivings. He knew how unhappy she was, and he was wretched because he had to acquiesce in Lady Westmorland's treatment of her. He dare not protest. It would not help the poor girl, and it might ruin him. Lady Westmorland would be a formidable enemy in the circle on which he depended for his livelihood.

He had learned Miss Montgomerie's story at last. For a long time rumour had said that she was the illegitimate daughter of a defunct Scottish baronet, by a governess. One day after lunching at the Palazzo Rospigliosi, Severn walked home with General Lord William Bentinck, who had commanded the British Forces in Sicily during the Napoleonic Wars. Lord William expressed himself very strongly about Lady Westmorland's behaviour towards her ward. She had burst into tears and rushed from the room when her ladyship had rated her, together with a footman, for leaving an inlaid sewing-table out on the terrace during a thunderstorm.

"Damned bad taste in front of guests! Damnable bad taste, anyhow, berating that sweet little girl along with a flunkey. Poor child! I can't think why Lady Lamb let her come, but who would believe that our hostess, who is brilliant and charming, would behave in this fashion?"

"Lady Lamb? Is Miss Montgomerie related to her, my lord?"

"No; not exactly. Look'ee, Severn, how much do you know?"

"Only vague rumours, sir. I am really not curious— only—only—I—she——" stammered Severn.

Lord William gave him a sharp look. "I suppose you're in love with her, you young dog? Who wouldn't be?" he cried.

"I've not thought of Miss Montgomerie in that way," said Severn. "But I wish I could help her. Lady Westmorland's attitude is so singular. I admire her very much. I am indebted to her, but——"

"But she behaves like the jealous egotist she is. By God, she does! Look'ee my boy, you must have heard rumours. I'll tell you the truth. The poor child's a bastard and, worse, an orphan. When I come to your studio to-morrow I'll tell you the story, confidentially. You know, I'm leaving Rome in a few days. I've been made Governor of Bengal. Egad! I wish I could do something for the girl. Perhaps you can."

Lord William called at the studio the next morning. He was a bluff, genial soul and delighted Severn by buying all of his Genzano vintage sketches. He examined the miniatures. "Why don't you make one of young Betty? You'll never find a prettier face," he said. Later he told Severn her history.

Her father, Major-General Lord Archibald Montgomerie, the heir of the Earl of Eglinton, had been on General Bentinck's staff in Sicily. Some years before he went there with his regiment he had a liaison with a lady who gave birth to his daughter, and died in childbirth. Before sailing for Sicily young Montgomerie married his cousin, Lady Mary, aged sixteen. The girl-bride went with him to Sicily, where their son was born, in 1812. The next year General Bentinck left Palermo for the war in Spain. He returned to Sicily after the Battle of Ordal, in which the expedition had suffered heavily. Lord Montgomerie had gone with the General. In Spain he fell ill with lung trouble and died at Alicante. Just before his death he called in Lord William, told him of his natural daughter, gave him a letter for his wife, and begged him to persuade her to look after the child. Lady Montgomerie left for England with her infant son as soon as Lord William had returned to Palermo. She promised to take the girl and bring her up with her own boy. The following year she married again, Sir Charles Lamb, Lord

P

Lieutenant of Ireland. Four years later the Earl of Eglinton died and her seven-year-old son became the thirteenth Earl, inheriting a famous castle and estate. As Elizabeth grew up, her presence in Scotland as the illegitimate half-sister of young Eglinton became embarrassing. At this stage her dead mother's friend, Lady Westmorland, had volunteered to take the girl with a view to adoption. A foreign residence made the proposition even more attractive. And so Elizabeth Montgomerie left for Rome.

"It's a sad story," said the General, "complicated by Lady Montgomerie's second marriage and a half-brother who's a peer. I doubt if the poor girl's any money of her own. Montgomerie had no time to straighten out his affairs. He went out like a candle in a gale."

IV

One evening in May, as Severn was returning to the Vicolo dei Meroniti after conducting the celebrated Dr Arnold of Rugby and some pupils through Prince Doria's gallery, to which the Prince kindly gave him access, he was astonished to see Miss Montgomerie. She came out of a street near the Fountain of Trevi. Severn's attention had been attracted by the voices of hucksters pestering a foreign girl. He was amazed and indignant on recognising her. It was an unheard-of thing for any gentlewoman to walk in the filthy streets of Rome. In no case dare she go unescorted, and never in the failing light. The brief Roman twilight was followed by an intense darkness in the cavernous unlit streets. Brigandage on the highways and murder in the by-streets were a commonplace of the Papal State. A lazy and corrupt guard offered small protection in a city of frightful poverty, of dark basements in which swarmed the lawless and the diseased. Even dead Popes had to be unostentatiously spirited away by night, attended by armed guards, lest an outraged populace vented its anger upon the corpse. Violence was met by official violence.

Two months ago Severn, crossing from the Prata meadows by a Tiber ferry, had come upon a horrifying spectacle in the great Piazza del Popolo. His curiosity aroused by a vast crowd, he was pinned in before he realised that there was to be an execution on a scaffold built in the centre of the piazza. Presently he saw the procession of the condemned. A curly-headed youth of eighteen, handcuffed, naked from the waist up, stood in a cart, two cowled monks holding a crucifix before him, seeking vainly to induce a confession. In tears, the condemned youth loudly protested his innocence. On arrival he was blindfolded and forcibly pushed up on to the scaffold.

Severn learned that the youth had been accused of the murder of a monsignor in whose house he was a servant. He had been condemned to death *per mazzola*, death with a hammer. A burly executioneer awaited the victim, a heavy mallet in his hand and a large knife at his waist. He began by forcing the screaming lad to his knees and then beat in his skull with the mallet. Severn shut his eyes, sick in the stomach at the horrific spectacle. Not a sound came from the sullen crowd. Few believed that the lad was guilty. When Severn opened his eyes it was to see the butcher thrust his hand in the skull and scatter the brains on the scaffold. Then with a knife he cut off the lad's head and proceeded to amputate the arms and legs, the scaffold streaming with blood, the executioner crimson. Having packed the amputated limbs, he then covered the remains with a mat. Severn fainted. When someone picked him up the crowd was streaming away. It muttered angrily against the Pope's cruelty in refusing a pardon. Crimes against priests were punished with the utmost savagery.

Two weeks later, as Severn again used the ferry, he heard a guitar being played and a man gaily singing to the customers of a little *osteria*. He recognised by his hair and boots the former executioner, singing with great gusto. Rome was still cowed and sullen from that official savagery. An outbreak of crime swept the city, the lawless element profiting by the disinclination of the public to assist the papal police. Robberies and murders made the back streets perilous even in daytime.

For this reason, Severn was horrified to see Miss Montgomerie out alone and on foot in the fading light. He hurried up to her and was welcomed eagerly.

"My dear Miss Montgomerie," he said, having scattered the hucksters, persistent to a point of menace, "what are you doing here alone? Don't you realise how dangerous it is? You must never come out on foot alone after daylight!"

Frightened, he saw her mouth tremble.

"I had an errand to do for Lady Westmorland. I couldn't find the place for some time," she explained.

"Lady Westmorland has no right to send you out on such errands. Surely she knows the risk? Why didn't she send you in her carriage?"

"Please, Mr Severn, don't be angry. And thank you," said Miss Montgomerie, recovered now from her agitation.

"I am going to take you home. It's getting dark."

At the corner of the street he called a carriage. It was the first time he had found himself sitting alone with her. They drove in an embarrassed silence. He wanted to let his hand go down on the seat and cover hers but, fearful lest she might resent the advantage he was taking, he restrained himself. At the gateway to the Palazzo Rospigliosi she broke the silence. It was now quite dark.

"If you please, Mr Severn, don't drive in. It is safe now. Thank you!" she said.

He stopped the carriage at the gate and rang for the porter. In the moment before the wicket gate opened a wild impulse surged over him. He caught her hand and, bending, kissed it passionately.

"Forgive me!" he cried, dropping her hand as the gate opened.

She made no reply, but before she turned away he caught a glimpse of her face. It was serious, with a wonderful light in her eyes.

"Good night and thank you!" she said simply, and was gone.

He got back into the carriage in a state of tumult. All the way home his heart beat madly. He knew without any doubt that he loved her, loved her as he had never loved anyone before.

CHAPTER XIII

I

THEY had a precious secret now. Although no word was said, each was conscious of their mutual passion. Fortunately, Lady Westmorland, infatuated with herself, could not conceive that she was not the centre of everything. Even others detected the love-drama proceeding under her nose.

One day Lady Compton, Scotch and downright, tackled him. "Why don't you marry Elizabeth? Run off with her if need be!"

"How can I? My living is here. Lady Westmorland could ruin me. And she might carry Elizabeth away. I must have time to save money. Another year and my position will be stronger."

"Have you asked her to marry you?"

"No. She is under a terrible strain now. I won't do anything to increase it. We must play for time," said Severn. "Thank God, Lady Westmorland's going away and leaving Elizabeth here."

Alas! in a few days Lady Westmorland changed her mind, as so often before. She seemed to grow more and more erratic every day. She announced that she would stay in Rome all the summer. She was seeing a great deal of Monsignor Reid, of the Scots College, a handsome priest who was now much the vogue. But at the end of July, after enduring the heat, she suddenly decided to go to Naples, where she had rented a villa for two months. She took it for granted that Severn would accompany her. The prospect both alarmed and attracted him. Could he live in such close proximity with Elizabeth and not betray the true state of things? He took the risk, however, and they all departed for Naples, Lady Westmorland, Severn and Miss Montgomerie in the first carriage, the servants and the baggage in three conveyances following.

Ten miles out of Gaeta they just escaped brigands. A lady and gentleman, reduced to their underwear, sat on the roadside with an hysterical maid and a dead groom near their horseless carriage. The lady's finger had been amputated by one ruffian hastily seizing her diamond ring.

On arriving in Naples, Severn was dismayed to find that the villa was the one in which he had visited the Walkers. By the end of August the situation became unendurable. Lady Westmorland's demands on him, her harsh behaviour towards her ward, the constant strain of keeping from her any knowledge of their shared secret made him decide to return to Rome.

He found the city on his arrival agog with a new sensation. The Monsignor for whose murder the lad had been *mazzolated* last March had been murdered by a priest in his household, who had now made a deathbed confession. The wretch had been present at the lad's execution and had witnessed it with no qualms. The news of the confession had caused the Pope to faint. He had abolished any further executions by *mazzola*.

In October Lady Westmorland arrived home, and a little later Henry Fox, whom she had not seen for a year, returned in company with a friend, Edward Cheney. Devoted to each other, they took an apartment. Fox had been in Florence where he had met the Blessingtons, D'Orsay and Lamartine the French poet. He brought with him some scandal. Blessington had sent for his daughter, Lady Harriet Gardiner, the girl of sixteen offered in marriage, or alternatively with her sister, to D'Orsay, according to the Will in which she was practically disinherited if she refused the hand of her stepmother's lover.

The British Minister, Lord Burghersh, outraged by this proposed sacrifice of the girl, refused to perform the marriage ceremony. The arrangement between the complaisant Earl, his adulterous wife and her lover seemed to Burghersh quite monstrous. He took refuge in a subterfuge. Since there must be a dual ceremony, according to the Catholic and Protestant rites, he insisted that the Church of England should have precedence. It was an affront to the French Minister, a devout Catholic and a particular friend of the Blessingtons, who were thus frustrated.

Fox had been a short time only in Rome when the "Blessington circus" arrived. Enraged by Burghersh's refusal, the Earl closed down his palazzo on the Arno at Florence. A friendly British Consul in Naples had offered to perform the marriage ceremony. Arriving in Rome, Blessington took the suite of rooms in the Villa Negroni once occupied by Lady Westmorland.

One morning outside the Caffé Ruspoli Severn encountered Henry Fox. He was very agitated and invited him to take coffee in the pretty little garden with its vine pergola and fountain. After a few minutes Fox unburdened himself.

"I've just had a visit from D'Orsay. As Burghersh in Florence won't marry him to that child-victim, they are perpetrating the crime in Naples! The fellow had the damned effrontery to ask me if I'd go as a witness! I've never set myself up as a moralist, but there are some things that I boggle at. I told him very bluntly what I thought of the whole business. That's one thing. Lady Westmorland's a great crony of yours, isn't she?"

"I should say not more than yours," said Severn guardedly.

"Well, I don't suppose you've ever received anything from her like this," he said, pulling four letters out of his pocket. "For some reason she's taken a violent antipathy to my friend Cheney. She insists that I break my association with him! Just read them. Then tell me if she isn't mad!"

Severn read the letters. They were written in terms of violent abuse of Cheney and Fox. When he had finished, he gave them back to Fox.

"You won't reply, of course? I should burn them," he said. "I begin to wonder if Lady Westmorland is quite sane."

"So do I. I suppose we shall meet at her ball to-night —it's going to be a big affair. She'll be the wittiest and most striking woman there and no one will believe that I've twenty-five pages of abuse from her in my pocket. She's a brilliant woman, but she's really a dreadful friend. She tears everyone to pieces and in the same breath assures you that she detests gossip. Her latest hobby is Catholicism—I believe she'll 'go over.' "

"And come back," commented Severn. "She talks of going into a retreat! A week will cure her of that! It is all very difficult. I owe a great deal to her. She can be very kind."

"And very cruel, as you know," said Fox. "The way she pushes around that poor little Elizabeth! Well, here we are gossiping also. I must go. Teresa Guiccioli's lunching with me. I'll see you to-night."

The ball at the Palazzo Rospiglioso was the finest spectacle Severn had seen since one given earlier that winter by Prince Doria. Lady Westmorland was magnificently dressed. All her jewels this night were emeralds. She was beautiful and gracious, a perfect hostess in a superb setting.

Severn looked in vain for Elizabeth all the evening, and when he had an opportunity of inquiring about her, at some risk of invoking displeasure, Lady Westmorland replied amiably, "The poor child has a dreadful headache and is keeping to her room."

A few days later Captain Daniel Roberts came to Rome, driving a gig from Florence. He had built the *Bolivar* for Byron and the *Ariel* for Shelley. The *Ariel* had been salvaged by him and re-rigged. Severn took him to see the graves of Keats and Shelley. Lady Westmorland gave a dinner party for him to which she asked Severn, Fox, Eastlake, Lady Deerhurst and Miss Leveson-Gower. It was the first time Severn had seen Elizabeth since the ball. He expressed the hope that she had recovered from her headache. She looked at him in surprise. Then he learned that Lady Westmorland had prevented her from attending the ball. "She said my dress was hideous, and she wouldn't let me make a spectacle of myself. I had dinner in my room," explained Elizabeth.

The small dinner party was almost a tragedy. While they were at the table one of the candles on the piano in the large salon set fire to the music and two Genoese velvet curtains went up in flames. Severn remembered the evening chiefly because Roberts was induced to tell the story of Shelley's last hours. He had warned Shelley of an impending storm, but the poet insisted on sailing for his home at Lerici. Trelawny tried to follow in the *Bolivar*, but the Leghorn harbourmaster would not give him port clearance. Roberts, seeing a sea fog come up, mounted a tower on the jetty and anxiously watched the *Ariel* through his spy-glass. He saw her far out at sea disappear into the fog—to meet an end no one lived to narrate.

The day following the dinner party Roberts met Severn in the Caffé Greco and asked him, "Who is Miss Montgomerie? Lady Westmorland treats her like a kitchenmaid."

II

By the end of January a feud had developed between Lady Westmorland and the French Ambassador, the Duc de Laval-Montmorency. He had given a ball to which he had invited the Blessingtons and D'Orsay. Declaring that it was an insult to all decent people to invite Lady Blessington and her lover, Lady Westmorland ostentatiously left the ball.

"They were dressed as gorgeously as Turks, but Lady Blessington looked like one of her profession," said Fox to Severn, who had not been present. Nevertheless, Fox rode with D'Orsay in the Villa Borghese the next day and dined with the Blessingtons and Countess Guiccioli.

Lady Westmorland demanded an apology. The Duc declining, she then tried to induce her countrywomen to boycott the French Ambassador. It was a plot on his part to humiliate the English aristocracy, she asserted. Declaring that Society had become too wicked to mix with, Lady Westmorland set off for a convent at Palo, fifteen miles up the Via Aurelia, where she stayed in seclusion for a week, praying and fasting. She went so suddenly, informing no one, that Severn, on calling at the Palazzo, learned of her departure from Elizabeth.

It was the day before the beginning of Carnival, which she had never seen. After much persuasion, Severn prevailed on her to let him take her to see it. The next day he called for her and they drove down to the Carnival, which began at noon. The bell on the Capitol tolled as a signal for the opening of the festivities. Never had they seen such crowds, such animation. The whole length of the narrow Corso from the Piazza del Popolo to the Piazza Venezia was a mass of people and carriages. It seemed as if every house, palace and office burgeoned with balconies trimmed with coloured pennants, hanging draperies, baskets of flowers and lanterns for illumination in the evening. Every window, balcony and roof was crammed with spectators who looked down on the seething mass of people. All were in fancy costume, masked. There were Punchinellos by the dozen, kings, queens, jesters, witches, grotesque beggars, students in foreign garb, etc. The centre of the Corso was reserved for carriages, one line proceeding on the left, one opposing it on the right. Royalties and ambassadors had the privilege of a centre track. Severn's coachman somehow wedged his way into the stream. The pretty women, that they might be acclaimed, sat on raised seats in the carriages. They were assailed by cries not always decorous.

At first Elizabeth seemed afraid. A dozen masked youths, seeing a beautiful young girl with the finest of complexions and luscious dark ringlets framing her masked face, attached themselves to their carriage and pestered her with attentions. A wild battle of sugarplums began. They were that only in name, for custom had substituted a mixture of sand covered with powdered marble and chalk which, breaking on the victim, whitened and almost blinded him. Soon everybody was splashed with white. The surging crowds, the costumes, the trumpets, rattles, whistles, confetti and cries all expressed a Saturnalian festival that had not died from the Roman scene after two thousand years.

But all this was only a preliminary to the races and the outbreak of the evening's bacchanalia. The costumes were highly fantastic. Women were dressed as men and men as women. Nymphs, pages, gnomes, satyrs, gods, goddesses, devils, judges, ballerinas, acrobats, cavaliers—the pageant was endless. It was a people's festival from which the Papal Guards and the authorities withdrew.

In the late afternoon, fatigued, Severn took Elizabeth to his studio. Only once had Lady Westmorland brought her there. Now she saw his sketches and was thrilled by his miniatures. He made tea. She was so animated, so free from the restraint imposed upon her, that never had she seemed so lovely, so adorable in her happiness. An enchanted hour passed before they returned to the Carnival for the races. As they were about to go, he said, "Why can't I paint you? You are so lovely in that Italian peasant's costume! You would be just right for my picture, 'The Fountain.' "

"But how could you? I couldn't get away."

"Elizabeth dear, why should you be a prisoner? You have a right to your life!" he protested.

She made no answer and looked down at her hands. When at last she raised her face there were tears in her eyes.

"Joseph, do not make it more difficult for me. I don't blame Lady Westmorland entirely. Women losing their youth get desperate and strike at anyone who reminds them of what they are losing. I think she means to be kind, but there's something wrong."

"Wrong! Of course there is! She's a hateful egotist. She must rule everyone!"

"I am afraid it is more than egotism. There's mental trouble. It frightens me sometimes, I am sorry for her. But don't let us spoil our day."

They discussed it no more and went down into the street. Princess Ruspoli had given Severn seats on her balcony overlooking the Corso. All the *beau monde* was there, masked. They saw Lady Blessington and Count D'Orsay drive by, and, later, Fox and Cheney with the Countess Guiccioli and a friend.

The carriages were now drawing to the side. The Papal Guards were clearing the course. The betting favoured Prince Torlonia's horses. At last the Governor rode by in his state carriage with a retinue. He was followed by the Senator, with another retinue. All Rome was hanging from the balconies, or on the tops of coaches or packed in temporary stands. As far as the eye could see, it was a river of vivid colours.

The riderless horses, fifteen in number, were coming at last. They had started from the Piazza del Popolo. They passed in a tumultuous burst of cheering, wild creatures frenzied by the cries and goaded by spiked balls hanging from chains that viciously stabbed their flanks. The moment they had passed the crowd surged on the Corso. They heard later that Prince Colonna's horse had won.

The light now rapidly failed. A thousand paper lanterns were lit. The Corso became a fairyland. Everyone carried a lighted wax taper. There were tapers on the coaches, on the crowns of hats, on poles, on balconies. The mad carnival of *moccoletti* began, everyone attempting to put out each other's taper. "*Sia ammazzato!*" they cried, uncontrollably.

"What does it mean?" asked Elizabeth.

"It's not pleasant to translate, really. It means 'Be murdered!' It's an Italian expression of mock violence," explained Severn. But as he told her this the word and the wish recalled that horrible *mazzolata*, the slaughter by mallet of the innocent lad in the Piazza del Popolo. Towards eight o'clock he drove Elizabeth home.

"The happiest day of my life, Joseph," she said as he took farewell of her.

"I shall remember it for ever!" he said in response.

He did not go home. He was too excited. He went back into the mob along the Corso. There he ran into Eastlake and Catherwood. Later, Fox and Cheney, with six girls crammed in a carriage, hailed them. It was five in the morning when at last they turned homewards.

CHAPTER XIV

I

LADY WESTMORLAND came back from Palo three days after the Carnival had ended. Fox had taken a villa at Frascati, and on the Sunday he invited her to lunch. She arrived an hour late, and could talk of nothing but Laval and D'Orsay. They were wicked men conspiring to ruin her. She had a mission to rid Rome of such depraved creatures.

"God must manifest Himself more plainly!" she cried. "I cannot fight His battles any more. There must be another Incarnation. I have said, 'God, manifest Yourself!' I have done all I can for the cause of virtue. God must complete the work!"

"Yes, yes," said Fox as they walked by a parterre. "What do you think of my water-clock?"

He pointed to a clock over the baroque fountain in the garden. It was operated by water filling ladles that oscillated from its weight.

"You do not care! You do not listen! Men are all alike! England and morality are held to scorn! You should challenge Laval to a duel!"

"Dear Lady Westmorland, I am a very poor duellist, and the Pope forbids duelling in his state," he answered.

Lady Westmorland stamped her foot with anger. "You are pro-French, of course! No wonder Pauline Borghese left your mother her library and Napoleon his snuff-box!"

Happily, just then his other guests joined them. Fox withheld his retort.

A few days later D'Orsay, exasperated by Lady Westmorland's campaign against him and the Blessingtons, wrote her a letter. It was violent in tone and ended by threatening to insult and outrage her. With this letter she called on Severn, and found him out. She hurried on to Henry Fox. His valet said he was not at home. Actually his master had just returned home for breakfast, after absence *chez* Guiccioli. She left word with the valet that she wished Mr Fox to call on her at the first possible moment.

Towards noon Fox arrived at the Palazzo Rospigliosi, very conscious that he could not assume the rôle of Paladin in Lady Westmorland's crusade for morality. He was received by a distraught woman in a dressing-gown, with her hair in disorder. She at once produced D'Orsay's letter and bade him read it. It was a shocking epistle.

"I am sending it to the French Ambassador. For the honour of his country, he must have D'Orsay expelled from Rome!" said Lady Westmorland, her hand shaking. He tried in vain to pacify her.

The next morning she was at his apartment again. He was in bed, but she thrust past the valet and entered his chamber. She was dressed in deep mourning: "For the wickedness of this world." She knew that God was working for her and she for Him. "For eighteen years I have suffered persecution! For eighteen years I have been reviled, ridiculed and libelled! Whom have I to thank for this? Lord Westmorland! Had he a grain of feeling, a spark of honour or a single Christian thought, what remorse he would feel now to see to what insults he has exposed the woman who bears his name!"

Suddenly Lady Westmorland fell on her knees by the young man's bedside, pressed her hands together and began to pray aloud. "Oh God, may he feel it, as he should, bitterly in this world. But spare him, spare him from remorse and sorrow in the next!"

Fox got out of bed, put on his dressing-gown and slippers and assisted Lady Westmorland to her feet. He rang for his man and asked for smelling salts. These he applied to the distraught woman. Recovered somewhat, she looked at him and said, "Henry Fox, you have put on your gown and slippers. When will you buckle on your sword for righteousness' sake?"

Before he could find any reply, she turned and looked out into his garden. "How wonderfully roses grow in Rome!" she observed calmly.

Fox rang for his valet and ordered biscuits and coffee for two. She began to describe the charades she was planning for her next party. She made no further reference to D'Orsay or Laval, and departed.

Fox made his protest in a stiff letter to D'Orsay. There at once came back to him a snuff-box that he had given D'Orsay in Florence. With it was a note accusing him of being *ingrate et faux*.

II

One morning, when Severn called on Lady Westmorland, he was received in her boudoir. The heat had been frightful for ten days. She was exhausted. On his way out Elizabeth, imprisoned for a week as her attendant, contrived to exchange a few words with him. She looked terribly fatigued. He did not see her again for a month. He had hoped to meet her at a ball the next evening, but he went down with a Roman fever.

Lady Westmorland departed to Florence on a visit to her stepson. She took Miss Montgomerie with her. She wrote at length to him, mostly ravings about suffering for righteousness' sake. He burnt the letters. Those from Elizabeth he saved. His letters to her went in envelopes addressed by his servant, lest Lady Westmorland should recognise his writing.

Soon after her departure she asserted that she had won her battle for morality. The Duc de Laval-Montmorency

Q

was being replaced as Ambassador by the Vicomte de Chateaubriand. The festivities at the Villa Negroni suddenly ceased. The Blessingtons announced their departure for Venice. The apartment that had seen so many grand entertainments given by Lady Westmorland and Lady Blessington was once more to let. The shade of the ill-fated Vittoria Accoramboni seemed to haunt its occupants.

Lady Westmorland had conducted her campaign with such scurrilous, wild letters, implicating all her friends, that no one would now have anything to do with her. Fox, disgusted by her insensate conduct, made a packet of her letters and sent them back to her, thereby ending all communication between them.

Severn saw much of Fox and Cheney in these weeks of Lady Westmorland's absence. He was invited out to the Villa Muti at Frascati, which they had leased. It evoked memories of Henry, Cardinal Duke of York, who had owned it. Here had come his sister-in-law, the Countess of Albany, wife of Bonnie Prince Charlie. Her notorious liaison with Alfieri had resulted in the poet's being expelled from Rome by the Pope. Here the errant "Queen of England," as her husband insisted on her being styled, had dwelt under the surveillance of the Cardinal after her refusal to return to the Young Pretender.

In the great heat of midsummer Severn spent some pleasant days at the villa. But he was unhappy in mind, wondering how Elizabeth was faring in Florence in these days of her guardian's increasing dementia. Distraught with anxiety, he unburdened himself to Fox who had long surmised the truth.

"Marry her, Severn! Get her away from that crazy woman! I'll lend you this villa for the honeymoon."

Severn pointed out his financial predicament. His earnings would not permit him to support a wife in England. Here in Rome Lady Westmorland would be transformed into an implacable enemy. He was saving money now. In a year, perhaps, he could contemplate marriage.

There were interesting visitors to the villa. Hortense Beauharnais, ex-Queen of Holland, a skilled amateur artist, was making a portrait of Fox. While she painted she talked with the greatest indiscretion. Napoleon, she said, as she sat by the open window that had a superb view of Rome beyond the flat Campagna, had always doubted his capacity to father a child. One day his sister Caroline procured for him a young girl who became pregnant after their association. Napoleon was elated until he learned that she had received Murat. He would not believe that the child was his. Then, in Poland, he had the intrigue with Madame Waleska. It was her condition that satisfied him of his powers, and he thereupon decided to divorce Josephine and marry for the sake of a dynasty.

Countess Guiccioli came and talked of Byron. Lord Dudley Stuart's affair grew more and more complicated. The Princess Christine had obtained her annulment, it seemed, only when Count Posse had submitted to an examination in proof of his impotency. He had consented to this after Lord Dudley had paid him £5,000. Now Madame Mère and the Bonapartes in Council had refused to recognise his civil marriage, and had summoned him to have a Catholic ceremony. The Pope had urged that the child be brought up in the Faith. The Bute family refused to recognise the child or to receive his wife.

"You see, if I have that second marriage it will make my child a bastard in the eyes of the Church," exclaimed Lord Dudley, "And that I refuse to do! Poor Christine! Lady Westmorland has been to see my wife and child in Florence and was charming to them."

"Then we'll have to credit her with one good deed," observed Fox, looking at Severn. "It's preposterous! Madame Mère receives Prince Jerome, whose Catholic marriage with Miss Patterson in Baltimore wasn't recognised by Napoleon. He made Jerome marry a German princess, by whom he has two sons and a daughter. Everybody knows that Mrs Patterson-Bonaparte's son is Prince Jerome's legitimate heir, and that all his other children are bastards, since Pius VII refused to annul the Baltimore marriage. My dear Dudley, don't let old Madame Mère bastardise your boy. Stick to your guns!"

III

In the last week of June Lady Westmorland returned to Rome. Severn called on her at once. He had a few words with Elizabeth, who promised to call at his studio the next morning if she went out on errands. Then her ladyship came in. She was annoyed to find them talking and at once invented a task to get rid of her ward. She was in a triumphant mood.

"God listens to prayers, Mr Severn! He chastens the wicked and supports the righteous! The Blessingtons have gone. Laval is dismissed!" she cried.

It was a singular interpretation, thought Severn. The Duc de Laval-Montmorency had been appointed Ambassador at Vienna. It was a promotion, since Vienna was the most important post in Europe after London. Severn did not dash her jubilant spirits by telling her so, nor did he point out that Laval's successor was the most notorious libertine in France.

Chateaubriand's appointment was an official return to Rome. It was in strong contrast to his miserable position twenty-five years earlier. Then he had arrived as a young secretary to the French Ambassador, Cardinal Fesch, Napoleon's wily uncle, who had forbidden him to seek an audience of the Pope. He had defied that order, and had also erred by calling on the ex-King of Sardinia. For his temerity, Fesch banished young Chateaubriand to a flea-infested attic in the Embassy. There he was given nothing more important to do than sign passports. The celebrated author of *Le Génie du Christianisme*, precocious, vain, ambitious, sensual, fretted at this humiliation. He also felt it keenly that with his miserable salary he could not support a carriage. He had arrived exulting. "My job is delightful! Nothing to do, master of Rome, I'm spoiled, belauded, made much of." But that mood soon changed. His clash with Cardinal Fesch, whom he had rashly disparaged in a letter to Napoleon, reduced him to a resentful nonentity. A former mistress who had followed him to Rome, died in a house that he took for her in the Piazza di Spagna. Even with the drawbacks of a wife in Paris who detested his writings, he pined for home. Happily Sion, in Valais, needed a *chargé d'affaires*, since Bonaparte desired to build a road to Piedmont through the little independent republic. Despite Cardinal Fesch having called him an intriguer, likewise a bad man, Napoleon appointed him. "For God's sake deliver me from Rome quickly. It is killing me!" cried Chateaubriand to a friend in office. He was delivered.

How different now was his triumphant return! A peer of France, Minister of State, Knight of the Golden Fleece, he was going to dazzle Rome with sumptuous entertainments. Pope Leo received him at once, refused to let him kneel, and made him sit beside him. His Holiness knew well that the author of *Le Génie du Christianisme* had changed into so doubtful a champion of the Church that he had said that if Christianity showed itself incompatible with liberty he would cease "to regard as true a religion which was opposed to the dignity of man." It had been thought that this statement might prevent the assent of the Vatican to his appointment, but the Papal Nuncio in Paris had written that "were the Holy See to refuse him, M. de Chateaubriand, whose vanity is potent, and whose self-esteem is touchy, might wage ruthless war against us. I would add that many wise and godly people here believe that the choice would turn him into a writer full of zeal for the good cause." The Pope realised the wisdom of this and gave Chateaubriand a most cordial welcome to Rome.

So Lady Westmorland's embodiment of an answer to prayer arrived. Mrs Bunsen did not subscribe to her opinion of the elegant roué of sixty. "I've had my curiosity gratified and seen Chateaubriand," she told Severn one day. "He is a vain creature, thinks himself handsome but I have to say that when he speaks French it is a treat to hear him."

The new Ambassador had been compelled to bring his wife with him, which did not prevent his writing to the adored Madame Récamier: "I love you, my letters will own it often . . . remember that we must and shall end our days together." To the Marquise de Vichet, an admirer whom he had never seen, he wrote, "Come to me!" She replied, sensibly, that she could not travel alone in a strange country. "Good morning, my lovely Léontine, my sylph, my unknown charmer, love me and write to me!" he cried to another admirer. In Rome he found consolation with the Countess Drago. He called also, dressed in the height of fashion, exquisitely mannered, on Mademoiselle Allart, French, twenty-five, amorous, and laid himself at her feet.

Such was Lady Westmorland's answer to prayer. But she knew and cared nothing about Chateaubriand. Like Salome, she danced triumphantly with Laval's head on her charger. And the monstrous D'Orsay and his mistress had been drummed out of Rome.

The next morning towards noon when he had almost despaired of her coming, Severn heard a tap on his door and saw Elizabeth standing there. The moment she entered he knew she was in a state of distress. There had been a dreadful scene with her ladyship, who had accused her of deceit. She wanted to know what she had been talking about with Severn when she had interrupted them last evening. She charged her with meeting or communicating with her enemies. She demanded to know whom she spoke with when she went out, and where she had been. Twice Elizabeth's letters had been opened—by accident, said Lady Westmorland. She had learned from the butler that he had been instructed to take all letters to her ladyship's room first. She had refused to allow her to accept invitations to balls at Prince Jerome's, at Lady Deerhurst's and even to a tea-party at the British Embassy. She vowed they were all enemies.

"I can't go on! I can't go on!" cried Elizabeth. "I am a prisoner. She is a wicked woman—no, not wicked—demented! I dare not come here any more; she is terribly suspicious. She made a frightful scene in Florence when someone said they had seen me riding with you at the Carnival. For three days she wouldn't speak to me. She says the most scandalous things about Mr Fox, who refuses to meet her. If I stay there any longer I shall lose my senses. Joseph, I am losing my senses! I must leave. I must go somewhere!"

She hid her face in her hands and burst into tears. He sat down and put his arm about her.

"We will find someone to whom you can go. You cannot stay there. Give me a few days. Let me——"

There was a knock on the studio door. Severn stood up and was about to go to it when there was another knock, more peremptory. His servant was out shopping. Something in the impatience of the caller alarmed him. He made a sign to Elizabeth and walked quietly to the window. Below in the street Lady Westmorland's carriage waited. The knocking was resumed. They waited. There was no further knocking. A few moments later he heard the carriage drive away.

"You see? She suspects I am here," said Elizabeth.

"No, no. It is just a call," he replied. "But it is monstrous! Why should you not be here? Why should we be afraid? We are not a pair of guilty lovers!"

He was trembling now in anger, not fear. He went and sat in front of the girl, taking both hands in his own.

"Elizabeth, give me a few days and we will get you out of that Palazzo. There must be someone to whom you can go—perhaps Mrs Bunsen, perhaps Lady Deerhurst."

"They will be afraid. Lady Westmorland will tell them the most dreadful stories about me. The things she says to me and calls me! It would be better to go to an Italian family. I have a small income, very small. I'd rather starve than continue like this."

He felt her tremble, and in his distress and love for her he wanted to take her in his arms, to comfort her, to kiss her tears away. He hesitated from delicacy, not wishing to presume on her distress.

"Give me two or three days and I will come and tell you what can be arranged. Trust me, Elizabeth. We must be very secret. She might decide suddenly to take you away."

Elizabeth stood up, composed again, and smiled at him.

"I do trust you, Joseph. Please don't make her your enemy. She would try to ruin you," she said.

"We may have to let her try. On Friday evening I will come to the palazzo. I shall have news for you."

She left him, and he watched her from the window cross the sunny street.

He got busy at once. But what had seemed so simple proved difficult. The heat of summer had emptied Rome.

The English colony had dwindled. Lady Compton was in Siena, Lady Deerhurst in Venice. The Bunsens were at the Villa Piccolomini at Frascati and Catherwood, Eastlake and Gibson were all away. Then he thought of Miss Leach and her brother Dr Leach, who lived in Rome in the winter and in summer went to Subiaco. They were kind, sensible people who kept away from the fashionable crowd. He wrote to them, but it would be impossible for him to have their reply by Friday.

IV

Severn was received very graciously by Lady Westmorland when he called at the Palazzo Rospigliosi. She insisted on his sitting down at the piano and playing a Mozart duet with her. All the time he listened for Elizabeth but there was no sign of her. He dared not inquire. At seven o'clock he left. Lady Westmorland was dining out. For half an hour he waited in the shadow by the gate until he saw it open and her carriage come out. Then he went to a *trattoria*, borrowed a pen and addressed a note to Elizabeth. He gave the porter at the palazzo gate a good tip to take it up to the house. He had asked Elizabeth to meet him in the Caffé Ruspoli the next morning from eleven to twelve.

But the next morning there was no Elizabeth at the Caffé Ruspoli. He waited until half-past twelve. She had been unable or was too afraid to come; or the note might not have reached her. It might have fallen into Lady Westmorland's hand. In that case he would never be allowed to see her. Her guardian would be insane with rage.

Severn was about to leave the pretty patio with its vine pergola and orange trees when Fox walked in. He was surprised to see him because he thought that he was at the Villa Muti.

"No. I've come in to see the water carnival in the Piazza Navona. Have you seen it?" asked Fox.

"No."

"Then you mustn't miss it. They flood the whole piazza and hold a water carnival in it. I hear it's most amusing. Why don't you come with me? We'll lunch there." Then, seeing Severn hesitate, he added: "You look very down—anything wrong?"

"Everything's wrong."

"Come along and you can tell me what it is. My gig's waiting."

They lunched at a restaurant overlooking the great rectangular Piazza Navona, the site of an ancient circus. It was surrounded by palaces. It had the Church of St Agnese on one side and, opposite, Bernini's great fountain surmounted by an obelisk. The whole Piazza had been converted into a lake. The elegant society of Rome was diverting itself by riding through it in carriages, the water spashing up to the axles. A crowd clustered on the balconies and at the upper windows. Naked urchins tumbled in and out of the water, begging for *soldi*.

The food was excellent, but Severn, obsessed by his problem, could not eat. He told Fox of the state of things at the Palazzo Rospigliosi, of Miss Montgomerie's resolution to get away, of the difficulty of finding a place for her, and of this morning's failure to keep a rendezvous.

"Of course the poor girl must get away," said Fox. "I will have nothing to do with that preposterous woman. What an extraordinary person! I never saw a manner so ladylike, so delightful when she wishes. One can't help finding pleasure in her company, despite the absurdity of her conduct. She can be generous and kind, as you know, but her fine impulses are perverted by vanity and her ungovernable rages. She suddenly sees an enemy in a friend who has given no offence, and then she becomes quite dangerous. How that poor girl has stood it all this time I can't think!"

"She's had to. She's not independent," said Severn.

"I know a little about that. Her position's certainly awkward, being illegitimate, which again gives Lady Westmorland a stick to beat her with. But she has a small allowance from her half-brother, Lord Eglinton. When he comes of age he might increase it. Their father, who was a friend of my mother's, died before he could make any provision for her. That's not the problem, however. Tell me frankly, Severn, aren't you in love with her?"

"Desperately!"

"She would marry you?"

"I've every reason for thinking so."

"Then take her away at once and marry her! That's the only solution. Why let money obstruct you? You can give her a home. I'd rather be dreadfully poor than dreadfully miserable. You've got your work, and I can't believe that Lady Westmorland can destroy you—she's too well-known. I'll back you, and if you really get in a fix I'm quite willing to help. So why not an Italian Gretna Green?" He banged Severn on the back and roared with laughter. "Yes, by God! Gretna Green—there's a kind of poetic justice in that! Lady Westmorland flung herself at that old curmudgeon Westmorland for title and position. He's always chased the money-bags. He ran off to Gretna Green with his first wife, heiress of old Banker Child, who was furious and cut her out of his Will. When she died he married our lady, a heiress twenty years younger than himself. That was a bad deal, actually. She's led him a devil of a dance. I had the whole story from Burghersh, his son in Florence, who was passed over, all the Child money going to his sister, Lady Jersey. So the Gretna Green abduction line is in the picture. Do it, Severn! You can honeymoon at the Villa Muti. It's time it had a respectable married couple after Alfieri's woman—and myself!"

He filled their glasses and raised his. "To your beautiful bride, Elizabeth Montgomerie!" he cried, forcing a smile out of Severn.

"To Elizabeth—my future wife!" responded Severn, raising his glass.

That evening Severn sent his servant with a note to Elizabeth, instructing him to wait outside until he saw Lady Westmorland drive out to dine at the Spanish Ambassador's, and then deliver it with his own hand. "Do not worry any more," he wrote to Elizabeth, "I am coming to the Palazzo to dine to-morrow night. I hope you get this note. Did you get my last? I waited at the Caffé Ruspoli. All will be well. I have a complete solution."

But Fate was fickle. The next day he went down with a Roman fever again. Three days later, when he was convalescing, Miss Montgomerie called at the studio.

"I've managed to get away for a few minutes, but I am watched all the time. Are you better?" she asked. "I couldn't get to the Ruspoli. Lady Westmorland kept me in all the morning. Joseph, I've come to tell you that we are going to Florence next week. What shall I do? I can't stay with her any more!"

"There is no need," he said, taking her hand in his. "I have a perfect solution, Elizabeth. I've found a place for you to go to—for ever. My darling, will you marry me?" he asked.

There was no answer, but instantly they were holding one another in a breathless embrace.

"Joseph," she said, after a few moments, "I can't be married in Rome—not from the Palazzo Rospigliosi. It has too many frightful memories."

"There's no necessity. Go to Florence with her. I'll

come to you there. My friend Brown can make all the arrangements for our marriage, secretly. Then I'll tell her and she can do nothing."

V

In the last week of September Lady Westmorland departed for Florence, where she had taken an apartment for the autumn season. Her household went with her. Chance played into Severn's hand. He was about to write to Brown when a letter came from him suggesting that he should come to Florence to convalesce after his attack of fever. Kirkup and Gibson were there. "Also Lady Westmorland. I trust that's no hindrance to your coming?"

Fox was there also and had written to him. Florence was very gay, the Burghershes and the Duchess della Rovere were entertaining. Lady Dudley Stuart, Teresa Guiccioli and her Florentine aunt, the Marchesa Sacrati, Mrs Patterson-Bonaparte, Prince Camillo Borghese, Louis Bonaparte and Lady Ashburton were all giving parties. "The Marchesa Sacrati at ninety-eight holds a reception in bedgown and nightcap. All the men are around her whist table at midnight. I made love to Teresa G. She fainted when she learned that my carriage was below. Said it would cause some *sospetto*—at that hour! Madame Vestris appears to-night in *Gli Originali*. When do your wedding bells ring? Lady Westmorland is here. Driving in the Cascini two days ago our carriages passed. We bowed, but did not speak. Miss Montgomerie shines so visibly that her ladyship will soon suspect something."

Severn was in Florence four days after receiving this letter. Brown had everything prepared for him. The marriage would take place in the British Consulate. Ironically, it would be performed by Lord Burghersh, the British Minister, stepson of Lady Westmorland. Kirkup was vacating his apartment for them to stay in until they left for Rome. Meanwhile, Severn stayed with Brown.

On Saturday morning early, Elizabeth Montgomerie went out shopping. She did not return to Lady Westmorland's apartment but met Severn at Kirkup's charming little palazzo overlooking the Ponte Vecchio. He was to act as best man. Gibson had insisted on providing the wedding feast.

Towards noon Severn left Elizabeth in charge of his friends to call on Lady Westmorland. She kept him waiting for half an hour. When she came in, with a rustling of silk petticoats, she was a wonderful apparition. She greeted him graciously.

"But what are you doing here in Florence?" she asked, when they were seated in the long salon.

"That is what I have come to tell your ladyship. To-morrow Miss Montgomerie will become my wife. We are marrying at the British Consulate," he said, quietly, clenching his fists.

The news must have surprised her, despite their apprehension of her suspicions. Her mouth opened, her eyes stared at him. Then she rose abruptly.

"Indeed! So, Mr Severn, I have been nourishing a viper—a pair of vipers! I should have known what might have come of playing benefactress to an ill-bred man and an illegitimate girl. You imagine you have tricked me. The whole world will hold you in contempt—vile, treacherous creature! I picked you up, I launched you in Rome, profitably despite your bad art, the crudeness of a music-teacher's son. That is the price of association with bohemians!"

While indulging in her tirade she pulled the bellrope. A footman entered.

"Tell the Signorina Montgomerie I require her at once," she said to him in Italian.

"Miss Montgomerie is not in the house, Lady Westmorland," said Severn. "She left you this morning. Henceforth she is in my care."

Lady Westmorland turned to the footman, her face blanched, her hands shaking.

"Show the Signore to the door!" she commanded.

Severn bowed and followed the servant.

VI

It was left for Lady Westmorland to give the wedding party a shock. When they had assembled in Lord Burghersh's office in a wing of the palazzo in which he lived, having been most graciously received by him, the door opened and a footman ushered in Lady Westmorland. She was dressed from head to foot in black silk. She had not a single jewel. Burghersh looked at her in astonishment.

"Since I am Miss Montgomerie's guardian, although I have no control of her any more, and disapprove of this marriage, for which my consent has not been asked, it is my duty, John, to perform my last act in that rôle. I shall sign the marriage register."

"That is your right," said Lord Burghersh coolly. "Shall we proceed?"

As soon as the brief ceremony was over, and the register had been signed by the bride and bridegroom and by Lady Westmorland and the other witnesses, even while Lord Burghersh was congratulating the wedded pair, Lady Westmorland departed without a word, her face set, her bearing expressing contempt in every line.

That same evening Joseph and his wife were about to go out to a performance of Lord Burghersh's opera *Feda*, for which Lady Burghersh had given them a box, when a letter was delivered at the palazzo, addressed to Severn. He knew the handwriting at once, and covertly went aside to open it. There were four sheets, hurriedly scrawled, full of slanderous abuse. They contained an accusation that the Eglintons had been obliged to send Elizabeth out of Britain owing to immoral conduct. As he read the vile epistle, Severn became tense with anger. Elizabeth, looking across the room, saw the expression on his face.

"What is it, darling? What is the letter you're reading?" she asked, coming towards him.

He turned and the expression on his face, the appeal in his eyes, told her at once from whom the epistle had come.

"What does she say?" asked Elizabeth, holding out her hand.

"No. It is not for your eyes. It is not for any decent person's eyes. It is filth!" he cried, hoarsely. Then he walked over to a secretaire on which candles burned and held the letter over one until it caught fire. When the last sheet had curled to black ash he went towards his wife, taking her in his arms, his lips resting like a benediction on her brow.

"My darling," he said with great tenderness, "nothing remains of the past. You have brought me everything I require of the future."

After a few moments together he released her, picked up her evening cloak, blew out the candles and, leaving, closed the door and escorted his young wife down to their waiting carriage.

THE END

POSTSCRIPT

POSTSCRIPT

READERS may wonder what happened with the passage of time to the characters of this novel. Here are some biographical details.

Severn, Joseph (1793–1879)

Following his marriage to Elizabeth Montgomerie, in 1828 he returned to Rome. The next three years saw him involved in a fraudulent claim by an Italian ex-servant. The corrupt Papal Courts gave a verdict against Severn. He fought the case courageously, at great expense, and finally, with the aid of the English Cardinal Weld and Chevalier Bunsen, got the verdict quashed, after heavy legal expenses. It was almost certain that the penniless Italian servant carried on the costly law case with money supplied by Lady Westmorland.

In 1829 while staying in Henry Fox's villa at Frascati his first child, a daughter, Claudia, was born; in 1830 came a son, Walter; in 1832, Ann Mary, in 1833, Henry. Four years later came another son whose christening was attended by Wordsworth, then in Rome. It was killed by falling out of its cot eight months later. In 1841 twins were born, Arthur and Eleanor.

The home life of the Severns was idyllic, though always hazardous in its finances, despite an allowance made to his sister by the Earl of Eglinton from the time of her marriage to Severn. Ann Mary became an artist of note, exhibited at the Royal Academy and was commissioned to make several portraits of the Royal Family. She married (Sir) Charles Newton, the discoverer of the great Mausoleum at Halicarnassus, which he excavated and transported to the British Museum. Three of Severn's children became artists. The twin son, Arthur, and his wife lived at Brantwood, Coniston, with the elderly Ruskin and nursed him in his decline. Eleanor married Henry Furneaux, and their daughter married F. E. Smith, later Lord Chancellor and first Earl of Birkenhead. Her granddaughter was Lady Eleanor Smith, the novelist.

Severn was *persona grata* with everyone in Rome except the English Catholics, annoyed because he refused to "go over" yet got Catholic commissions. Every distinguished English visitor to Rome called upon him as the best cicerone to the sights. They included Bulwer Lytton, then writing *Rienzi*, Mendelssohn, aged twenty-one, soon to be famous in England, the twenty-eight-year-old Gladstone, who proposed to his future wife in the Coliseum, the twenty-one-year-old Ruskin, travelling with his parents, Dr Arnold of Rugby and the dying Sir Walter Scott.

In 1841 after an absence of twenty-one years Severn and his family returned to England. With a wife and six children to support, and little success as an artist, he entered a precarious phase. It was lightened by a successful cartoon in the competition for the decoration of the new Houses of Parliament and the success of his daughter Mary. Nevertheless, they lived with gaiety in their improvidence. Callers at their London home included the Gladstones, Lord Lansdowne, Rossetti, Mendelssohn, George Richmond, Sir Charles Eastlake, and the Bunsens. They were always welcome guests at Eglinton Castle, the seat of Mrs Severn's half-brother. Twelve years after their return to London Severn was obliged to flee to Jersey to avoid pressing creditors. His financial straits were alleviated in 1860 by his appointment as Consul in Rome in succession to his son-in-law, Newton. The appointment was largely due to Bunsen who wrote from his death-bed to Gladstone. Severn was a very youthful sixty-eight at this time. It was a most popular appointment. Ruskin's earlier description of the new Consul still held good:

"There is nothing in any circle that ever I saw or heard of like what Mr Joseph Severn then was in Rome. He understood everybody, native and foreign, civil and ecclesiastic, in what was nicest in them, and never saw anything else than the nicest; or saw what other people got angry about as only a humorous part of the nature of things. It was the nature of things that the Pope should be at St Peter's, and the beggars on the Pincian steps. He forgave the Pope his papacy, reverenced the beggar's beard and felt that alike the steps of the Pincio, and the Aracœli, and the Lateran, and the Capitol, led to heaven, and everybody was going up, somehow; and might be happy where they were in the meantime. Lightly sagacious, lovingly humorous, daintily sentimental, he was in council with the cardinals to-day, and at picnic in the Campagna with the brightest English belles to-morrow; and caught the hearts of all in the golden net of his goodwill and good understanding."

Severn found in Rome his old friends, Overbeck and Gibson. He established himself in a lofty apartment overlooking the Fountain of Trevi. His wife followed him but falling ill at Marseilles, died there the day before the frantic husband could reach her. She was a devoted wife and mother, never dismayed by the vicissitudes of thirty-four years of happy married life with a feckless artist. Severn henceforth was much alone though intermittently visited by his children. He attended to his duties conscientiously and was unwearying in his art studies and his lifelong devotion to the memory and fame of Keats. He was saddened by the death of his gifted daughter, Mary, in 1866. A frequent visitor to his apartment was the Abbé Liszt, who played to him by the hour, but when Severn went away he took the precaution of locking up the piano, as Liszt was apt to break the strings. He was in Rome during Garibaldi's abortive march on the city and he was indefatigable in looking after Garibaldi's men who were taken prisoners. During this period he was overjoyed to have as a companion Madame de Llanos, Keats's favourite sister Fanny, then visiting Rome. With a united Italy, the Consulship ended in 1872. King Victor Emmanuel made him an Officer of the Order of the Crown. He received from the British Government a pension of £80 and a Civil List pension of £60. On this he contrived to live. He was attended by a devoted servant, Betta.

At eighty-four he was full of charm and vivacity. He rose at six, played the piano, painted and walked. His health failing in 1878, his son Walter went out to him. He died on August 3, 1879, aged eighty-six. His last painting was of John Keats and he was buried beside him in the Protestant Cemetery at Rome. His biography was written by William Sharp in 1892, a slapdash production full of errors that was superseded in 1943 by an excellent life, *Against Oblivion*, by Sheila Birkinhead.

Westmorland, Jane Fane, Countess of (1780–1857)

Married in 1800 as second wife, John Fane, tenth Earl of Westmorland, by whom she had four sons and two daughters. Soon after the death of her husband in 1841 she returned to

England and lived at Brympton, Somerset, on an estate bequeathed by the Earl to their daughter, Cicely. The Countess died there, aged seventy-seven and was buried at the Westmorland seat, Apethorpe, Northants.

Westmorland, John Fane, eleventh Earl of (1784–1859)

Son of John, the tenth Earl and of his first wife Sarah Child. As Lord Burghersh he was Adj.-General in Sicily and Egypt, 1806–7; A.D.C. to Wellington in the Peninsular War, 1808–1813; in the battles of Vimeiro, Talavera, Torres Vedras, and Busaco; Envoy Extraordinary and Minister Plenipotentiary to the Grand Duchy of Tuscany, 1814–1830; Privy Councillor 1822, Lieut.-General, 1838; Minister at Berlin, 1841–1851. He was mediator between Prussia and Denmark in the Schleswig-Holstein dispute; Minister to Vienna in 1851, and in 1855, with Lord John Russell, took part in the Congress of Vienna. He retired the next year. At Queen Victoria's command his last service was to convey her congratulations to Leopold, King of the Belgians, on the twenty-fifth anniversary of his accession to the throne.

He married in 1811, Lady Priscilla Anne Wellesley-Pole, daughter of the third Earl of Mornington. The favourite niece of the Duke of Wellington, she was an accomplished linguist and a distinguished artist. Her most famous painting is a portrait of Anne, Countess of Mornington, surrounded by her three famous sons, Richard, Marquis Wellesley, Arthur, Duke of Wellington, and Henry, Baron Cowley. She died in 1879. Her husband was so highly thought of in Berlin that on his death in 1859 the principal military bands, in the presence of the Prince Regent, played Beethoven's Funeral March. He was as distinguished a musician as he was a soldier and diplomat. An excellent violinist, he composed seven operas, numerous cantatas and an anthem. In 1823 he founded the Royal Academy of Music. He was buried at Apethorpe.

Bunsen, Christian Charles, Chevalier (1791–1860)

Born at Kirbeck, Waldeck. As a boy he read Hebrew, Arabic, Persian. He studied at Göttingen. In 1815 while in Berlin he so impressed Niebuhr that when he became Prussian Envoy to the Papal Court he made young Bunsen his secretary.

He married Frances Waddington in Rome in 1817 and by her had twelve children. Their home in the lovely Palazzo Caffarelli overlooking the Forum became a rendezvous of diplomats, musicians and artists. He succeeded Niebuhr at Rome, but after a collision with the Papacy on policy, he resigned in 1838. He spent two years as Ambassador in Berne and afterward was Ambassador to the Court of St James, 1842–1854. He strongly urged the Prussian King to throw in his lot with the western allies on the outbreak of the Crimean War. On the King's refusal and announcement of "benevolent neutrality," he resigned office. His sagacity and integrity were widely esteemed and the Bunsens were highly popular in England. His grandson, Sir Maurice de Bunsen, became a distinguished English diplomat.

Eglinton, Archibald Montgomerie, thirteenth Earl of (1812–1861)

Son of Lord Archibald Montgomerie. Born in Palermo, Sicily. He succeeded to his grandfather's titles and estates in 1819. As Viceroy of Ireland he was immensely popular for his liberality and kept up the Viceregal Court in princely style. In 1839 he held the famous Tournament at Eglinton Castle, described by Disraeli in *Endymion*. It cost £40,000. On the Turf he won the St Leger in 1842 and 1847, and the Derby and the St Leger in 1849. He was always cordial and generous to his half-sister, Elizabeth Severn, and to her family.

Gibson, John (1790–1866)

Born at Conway, Wales, the son of a market gardener, he revealed precocious gifts as a sculptor. He dreamed he was carried to Rome by an eagle, and patrons enabled him to go there in 1817, where he was most generously received by Canova. He studied under him and under Thorwaldsen and immediately took a high place in the Roman art world. He had innumerable commissions from the visiting English aristocracy. In 1844, famous, he visited England and was commanded by Queen Victoria to make a bust of her. He was in England again in 1850 when he made a statue of the Queen for the Houses of Parliament. He created a sensation at the International Exhibition in 1862 with his tinted Venus. He lived wholly for his art, generous, simple-minded. "He is a god in his studio but God help him out of it!" said a friend. He died in Rome in 1866 after a happy industrious life. "I worked all my days, happily, and with ever new pleasure, avoiding evil, and with a calm soul, making images, not for worship but for love of the beautiful." He was the last exponent of the old school of European sculpture. He refused to execute statues of Huskisson and Sir Robert Peel for Westminster Abbey unless allowed to drape them classically. "The human figure concealed under a frock coat and trousers is not a fit subject for sculpture," he said. He left his fortune of £32,000 and his works to the Royal Academy. Four of his classical figures decorate the stairway of the Diploma Gallery there.

Clark, Sir James (1788–1870)

The physician who attended Keats in Rome was born in Banffshire and entered the Navy in 1809 as Assistant Surgeon. He was twice shipwrecked. He took a consumptive patient to France and Switzerland, and settled in Rome where he practised until 1826. He then went to London and became physician to Prince Leopold, later King of the Belgians, who, in 1834, got him the appointment of physician to the Duchess of Kent, mother of Queen Victoria. The Queen on her accession made him Physician-in-Ordinary. He became a baronet in 1837 and was greatly esteemed until he was involved in the tragic case of Lady Flora Hastings, a Maid of Honour to the Queen. The growth of an abdominal tumour led to the accusation that she was pregnant. Sir James was called in to give a professional opinion following the girl's denials. An erroneous diagnosis resulted in her dismissal from Court. The unfortunate Lady Flora died later of her tumour. Clark lost popularity and much of his practice, but a man of great integrity he retained Court favour. He became a Fellow of the Royal Society in 1832. He died at Bagshot Park in 1870, in a house lent to him by the Queen.

Kirkup, Seymour (1788–1880)

The son of a London diamond merchant, he had ample means. In his youth he was acquainted with William Blake. Threatened by consumption, he settled in Rome in 1821 and was present at the funerals of Keats and Shelley. Later he moved to Florence and lived in a house near the Ponte Vecchio, overlooking the Arno. He became very friendly with Walter Savage Landor, knew the Brownings and was popular in Florentine society. He was a good artist but being under no financial pressure was somewhat of a dilettante. An earnest student of Dante, in 1840 with two friends he obtained permission to search for the portrait of the poet that was supposed to have been painted by Giotto in the chapel of the Podestà (Bargello). They found the portrait on July 21, 1840. It was almost ruined by bad restoration in 1841 but fortunately Kirkup had made a surreptitious sketch. This he gave to Dante Gabriel Rossetti.

In later life Kirkup grew more and more eccentric in dress and manner. Having received the Order of St Maurizio, he believed that it entitled him to be styled Barone and persisted in using this title. He became deeply interested in spiritualism and introduced the famous medium, David Hume to Mrs Browning whose husband, incensed by his influence over her, caricatured Hume in a poem *Mr Sludge, the Medium*. Kirkup, a Lothario, had, by a Florentine girl who died aged nineteen, a daughter. She married and died in 1878, leaving two children. Kirkup married in 1875, aged eighty-seven, a bride of twenty-two, the daughter of Signor Carboni, English Consul at Rome. In 1872 Kirkup moved to Leghorn and died there, aged ninety-two.

Westmacott, Richard (1799–1872)

Son of Sir Richard Westmacott, R.A., and grandson of a sculptor. He entered the Royal Academy School in 1818 and proceeded to Rome in 1820 studying there six years. In 1827 he exhibited at the R.A. his first statue, *Girl with a Bird*. He was elected Royal Academician in 1838. He carved the pediment of the Royal Exchange in 1842 and his statue of Archbishop Howley in Canterbury Cathedral is considered his finest monument. In 1857 he succeeded his father as Professor of Sculpture at the R.A., a post he held for ten years. He was the gifted son of a famous father who had studied under Canova in 1793 and who is remembered for his *Achilles* in Hyde Park, his *Duke of York* on the column in Waterloo Place, and for the portico of the British Museum, London.

Eastlake, Sir Charles (1793–1865)

Entered the Royal Academy School in 1809 and a year later won its Gold Medal. As an earnest student he read Homer and Virgil and was distinguished early by his industry and judgment. He was at Plymouth when Napoleon arrived there a prisoner on board H.M.S. *Bellerophon* and from a boat the young artist sketched the Emperor. From this sketch he produced a full portrait. It was exhibited with great success and brought him in £1,000. He departed for Rome in 1816 in the company of young Bunsen. He was fourteen years in Rome. He made a nine months' tour of Greece returning with sketches that made a sensation. He was regarded as the most industrious artist in Rome. He won early fame in London with his pictures of Italian bandits. He was elected a Royal Academician in 1839. His picture *Christ weeping over Jerusalem* created a sensation in 1841. Sir Robert Peel appointed him secretary of the Fine Arts commission for the decoration of the new Houses of Parliament, and he was also chief advisor in all art matters to the Prince Consort and the Government. He was Keeper of the National Gallery, 1843–1847 and was elected President of the Royal Academy in 1850.

Brown, Charles Armitage (1787–1842)

At the age of eighteen Brown went to St Petersburg to conduct a business he had inherited. Five years later he returned to London, ruined, the business having failed. He inherited a small income and on this and on journalism contrived to lead a bohemian life. With his fellow bachelor, Charles Dilke, he built a house, Wentworth Place, on the edge of Hampstead Heath. It was ingeniously divided. Here he lived in one half, Dilke in the other. During a summer vacation he let it to Mrs Brawne and her daughter Fanny. Keats stayed in this house both with Brown and with the Brawnes and it played a major part in his poetical history. Here he met and fell passionately in love with the eighteen-year-old Fanny. It was in this house that he called for Brown to bring a candle, and, examining some blood he had coughed up on his pillow, said: "That drop of blood is my death warrant. I must die."

Brown was waited on by an Irish maid by whom he had

a son, Carlino. He wrote a serio-comic opera that was produced at Drury Lane in 1814. It ran only a few nights. In 1822 he went with his son to live in Florence where he met Byron and struck up a friendship with W. S. Landor. Later, for a short time, he shared a house in Rome with Severn and then returned to Florence. It was from Brown's house that Severn went to be married. In 1835 he returned to England but, restless and unsuccessful, he decided to emigrate. He left for New Zealand with his son in 1841. The next year, still unsettled, he was preparing to return to England when he died. Gifted, humorous, kind, excellent company, loved by Keats, he never succeeded in his literary ambitions. Leigh Hunt described him as "one of the most genuine wits now living."

Bancroft, George (1800–1891)

Born at Worcester, Mass., U.S.A., he was the eighth of thirteen children. He entered Harvard at thirteen and five years later sailed for Europe. He studied at Göttingen, taking a D.Ph in 1820. He travelled in Europe extensively and met Humboldt, Goethe, Byron, etc. His meeting with Byron took place on board the U.S.S. *Constitution* at Leghorn and he called on him the next day at his villa where Bancroft was most cordially received and introduced to the Countess Guiccioli, Byron's mistress, whom he described later as having 'a lovely expression, a sweet mouth, a beautifully small waist, her face and manner all innocence and repose'. He was invited to stay to lunch and Byron told him that he wished to settle in America. "Perhaps I might find there the honour Britain fails to give me," he said.

In 1822 Bancroft returned to America and was appointed tutor in Greek at Harvard but his European experience produced a state of mind that irritated his narrow Harvard friends. He resigned and entered a partnership to found a preparatory school. In 1834 he published the first volume of a *History of the United States*. With the publication of the last volume he was established as a historian and famous. He entered politics and became in turn Secretary of War, and Secretary of the Navy under President Polk. For three years he was a highly successful Minister to the Court of St James. He formed close friendships with his fellow historians, Macaulay, Milman and Hallam in

England and with Guizot and Theirs in France. The sixth volume of his *History* occupied him from 1849 to 1867 and in that year he became U.S. Minister to Berlin where he stayed seven years. In 1874 at the age of seventy-four he issued the final volume of his *History* but he continued writing until 1885. At eighty-five he wrote to Oliver Wendell Holmes that he was "strong enough to rise in the night, light my own fire and candles, and labour with close application for fourteen hours consecutively, that is, from five in the morning till eight in the evening with but one short hour's interruption for breakfast, and otherwise no repast, not so much as a sip of water." Holmes retorted: "You must be made of iron and vulcanised indiarubber or some compound of resistance and elasticity."

Coolidge, Joseph (1801–1881)

The son of Joseph Coolidge of Boston, and seventh in descent from John Coolidge, immigrant, who settled in Watertown, Mass., in 1630. He was educated at Harvard and at the age of nineteen left for Europe. He called on Byron at Ravenna in 1821. The poet, writing to Moore, said: "I have here a friend of your Mr Washington Irving, a very pretty lad, a Mr Coolidge of Boston—only somewhat too full of poetry and 'entusymusy.' " To Murray Byron also wrote: "He was very intelligent, very handsome and not more than twenty years old according to appearances. A little romantic, but that sits well upon youth, and mighty fond of poesy as may be suspected from his approaching me in my cavern. He told me that he had obtained a copy of my bust from Thorwaldsen at Rome, to send to America. I confess I was more flattered by this young enthusiasm of a solitary transatlantic traveller than if they had decreed me a statue in the Paris Pantheon. . . . I say I was more flattered by it, because it was single, unpolitical, and was without motive or ostentation—the pure and warm feeling of a boy for the poet he admired. It must have been expensive, though. I would not pay the price for a Thorwaldsen bust for any human head or shoulders, except Napoleon's or my children's."

Coolidge returned to Boston in 1822. He married the granddaughter of Thomas Jefferson, third President of the U.S., and entered commerce with much success. He loaned the

Thorwaldsen bust of Byron for an exhibition at the Boston Athenæum Society in 1840. It was presented later to the Gardener Museum there by his youngest son, Thomas Jefferson Coolidge (1831–1920), merchant, financier, diplomat, who was U.S. Minister to France in 1892. Coolidge's great-nephew was Archibald Coolidge, the historian.

Ticknor, George (1791–1871)

After taking a degree at Dartmouth College, N.H., he went to Europe in 1815, and following the pattern of gifted young Americans studied at Göttingen University for two years. He was appointed to the Chair of Modern Languages at Harvard and went to Europe again in 1818, meeting there many of its most illustrious figures, Byron, Chateaubriand, Madame de Staël, Goethe, Scott, Wordsworth, etc. Wealthy, handsome, he charmed Byron, who opened his melodramatic heart to him, presented him with a volume of his poems, gave him a letter to the notorious Ali Pasha of Janina, a bloodthirsty tyrant, and a pistol with which to defend himself. Ticknor was one of the founders of the Boston Public Library and possessed the largest private library in the U.S. He again went to Europe in 1835 and three years later made an international reputation with his *History of Spanish Literature*. He wrote a life of his friend, Prescott, the historian, and was long a foremost figure in that famous circle of Boston intellectuals, Emerson, Longfellow, Holmes, Thoreau, etc. He died aged eighty.

Fox, Hon. Henry Edward (1802–1859)

Fourth and last Lord Holland, son of Elizabeth Vassell (Lady Webster) and the third Lord Holland, nephew of Charles James Fox, and Whig member of Lord Grey's and Lord Melbourne's Cabinets. After Severn's marriage Henry Fox lived at the Villa Muti, Frascati, formerly inhabited by the Cardinal Henry, Duke of York, for three years, continuing his relations with Byron's ex-mistress, the Countess Guiccioli. He wearied of and terminated this connection in 1830. "To have to make love without feeling a particle is sad work, and sad and serious I find it." The next year Fox entered the diplomatic service. He was British Minister at Florence,

1838–1846. He edited his father's *Reminiscences* and died in Naples in 1859 leaving no heir to the barony.

In 1923 Lord Ilchester edited Fox's *Journal* and released it for publication. The author is indebted to this volume for much of the characterisation given to Fox in this novel.

Stuart, Lord Dudley Coutts (1803–1854)

Eighth son of the first Marquess of Bute by his second wife, daughter of Thomas Coutts, banker. M.P., 1830. In 1831, after the visit of Prince Czartoryski to England, he became the passionate advocate of the independence of Poland, to which he devoted his life. He warned the allies of the danger of Russian aggression. He died in Stockholm while on a mission to persuade the King of Sweden to join the western Powers in the reconstitution of Poland. He married Christina, formerly Countess Posse, daughter of Prince Lucien Bonaparte, who died in Rome, after a separation, in 1847. Their son, whose birth created a Roman scandal, Paul Amadeus Francis Coutts, Captain of the 68th Regiment, died in 1889.

Bentinck, Lord William Charles (1774–1839)

The second son of the third Duke of Portland, was both soldier and statesman. From 1803 to 1807 he was Governor of Madras. He fought under Sir John Moore at Corunna and was with Wellington in Spain. In 1811 he went as Envoy to the Court of Sicily and was Commander-in-Chief of the British Forces there for three years. Among many reforms he instituted constitutional government despite the opposition of King Ferdinand. In 1813, he led an expedition of mixed forces to the east coast of Spain. After varying fortunes it suffered defeat at the Pass of Ordal. He re-embarked for Sicily on the threat of a landing there by Murat. In 1814 he made a successful expedition to Genoa where he issued a proclamation that anticipated Italian unity by fifty years. He returned to Palermo and left Sicily in 1814. In some disfavour by reason of his liberalism, he was unemployed at the close of the Napoleonic Wars and remained in Rome until 1828. He was then appointed Governor of Bengal. He converted a deficit into a surplus and effected administrative and educational reforms. He raised the official status of the natives, abolished suttee

269

(widow-burning), in 1829, and suppressed Thuggism. He had on his Administrative Council Macaulay, with whom he formed an enduring friendship. He became the first Governor-General of India in 1833. When he left two years later he was lamented by natives and Europeans alike. A statue of him was erected in Calcutta, with an inscription written by Macaulay. One of the great pro-consuls, he declined a peerage on retirement. He died in Paris in 1839.

Blessington, Marguerite, Countess of (1787–1847)

After the return of the "Blessington Circus" from Italy, Lord Blessington died in Paris in 1829. D'Orsay, soon separated from his wife, lived with the Countess until her death. Their home in Seamore Place, and later Kensington Gore, became the centre of a brilliant salon to which men of fame and genius flocked. She published many popular books, including *Conversations with Lord Byron*. In 1849 Count D'Orsay fled from England to escape his creditors and Lady Blessington, also embarrassed by debts, joined him in Paris where she died a few weeks later in straitened circumstances. The great dandy, wit, artist and benefactor of his distressed compatriots, died in Paris in 1852, a few weeks after his appointment as Director of Fine Arts.

Cavendish, William Spencer, sixth Duke of Devonshire (1790–1858)

Born in Paris, he succeeded to the dukedom in 1812. At the age of twenty-six he was sent to Russia on an official mission to attend the coronation of the Emperor Nicholas. He travelled to St Petersburg with a superb retinue that cost him £50,000 in addition to the government allowance. He had a serious disposition, with strong literary and artistic tastes. He employed Joseph Paxton as agent for his Derbyshire estates. At Chatsworth, on the Duke's orders, Paxton built the gigantic glass conservatory that he used later as a model for the crystal palace at the Great Exhibition, 1851.

The Duke added greatly to the famous collection at Chatsworth, and on coins and medals spent the sum of £50,000. He fulfilled the vow made to the Gallatins that he would never marry, and died in 1858, when the dukedom passed to his cousin, the second Earl of Burlington. An echo of the scandal surrounding his birth occurs in the *Journal* kept by the Hon. Mrs Calvert (*An Irish Beauty of the Regency*. John Lane.) under the date Feb. 14. 1818:

"There is nothing talked of but a story that the Duke of Devonshire is illegitimate; that he was not the late Duchess's son but Lady Elizabeth Foster's by the Duke, and was changed for the Duchess's daughter. The Duke married Lady E. Foster, who is now living in Italy, and they say Lord George Cavendish, who would be Duke if this is true, is gone abroad to enquire into it. Sir Richard Croft, who attended the two ladies, and was of course, if this is true, privy to it, shot himself yesterday morning while attending a Mrs Thackeray. Some say that he thought she would die, and that the recollection of Princess Charlotte's losing her life under his care produced insanity. Others say he was so hurt at the Prince's not speaking to him at the Levee that that produced it. Others again say it was shame at the discovery made of the share he had in changing the children. Be it as it may, however, he retired into a room where, unfortunately, were a pair of pistols, and shot himself."

Trelawny, Edward John (1792–1881)

Born in London, the son of Lieut.-Col. Trelawny, M.P., and Maria, daughter of Sir Christopher Hawkins, Bt. He entered the Navy at eleven, deserted, and, joining a privateer, had desperate adventures in the Indian and Malay seas before he was twenty. He returned to England in 1813 and married. In 1821 he went to Italy and met Shelley and Byron. He was to have gone with Shelley and Williams on the *Ariel* from Leghorn but was delayed and saw the ship disappear in a squall. He recovered the bodies and cremated them on the seashore at Viareggio, in the presence of Byron. After arranging for the final interment of Shelley, whose heart he had recovered from the flames, and paying for the widow's return to England, he joined Byron and sailed with him for Greece in 1823. Dissatisfied with Byron's delay in attacking the Turks, he joined the insurgent chief, Odysseus, and married, as his second wife, the chief's sister. Hearing of Byron's illness, he hurried to Missolonghi but arrived too late. His curiosity in peering beneath the shroud to ascertain the nature of the poet's lameness brought him severe censure. He returned to defend Odysseus's stronghold on Mt Parnassus and narrowly escaped assassination by a treacherous English colleague. A daughter, Zella, was born in 1826. He returned to England in 1828 and began an autobiography, *The Adventures of a Younger Son*, that brought him fame and was soon established as a classic of adventure. He visited the United States, and at Niagara Falls held up Fanny Kemble to see them, and swam the rapids. He lived awhile in Italy and finally settled in England.

Handsome in youth and old age, a vivacious raconteur, he sat as model for the sea captain in Millais's famous painting *The North-West Passage*. Swinburne dedicated to him *Songs of the Springtides* and wrote some memorial verses. He was painted by D'Orsay, Severn and Kirkup. When he died, aged eighty-nine, his body was cremated and, as requested, the ashes were placed in the grave he had prepared next to his hero, Shelley, in the Protestant Cemetery at Rome.

ARBROATH PUBLIC LIBRARY